MICKEY SOJOURN

JOSH LETTIERE

CONTENTS

ACKNOWLEDGMENTS

My L.A. crew and the homies in County blues…

A rogue's gallery, fuckin' A…ain't no other way…

The Warden of Tuffy's Gym…grillin' motherfuckers, then grillin' for em…

Albin Sikora…Albie you already know…

Marcello Mazzilli…here we go, kid…

Alverne Ball…a big money foreman if you ever saw one…

Joe Sikora…know you're more Chicago than L.A….but you Hollywood…you saw somethin in me, gave me new life…thanks man…

Philly "Boy" Donlon…I got cats…let's get them Zevon Bucks, my guy…

Dave "Maverick" Heffernan…always holdin' it down…for everyone…

Lanny Joon…the philosopher with fists of fury

Laura James…the splash of class on Ogden Avenue…

Chicago…my muscle back home…

Mikey Basile…alright alright, I know guy, you heard this story already!…you've always been there, love you guy…

Jake Callinan and Eddie Donoghue…to get to me…gotta get through them first…

Adom "DIZZ" Daniels…we made it this far…don't make no damn SENSE!!

Max Schmidt and Ryan Taylor and Brian Daly…the guys from way back…

Local 1 Ironworkers…my brothers up on the steel, hangin' and bangin'…

Special mentions

Kim Savo…I'll never forget the light you provided in the dark…

Joyce Hill…thanks for the typewriters and the beautiful letters in lockdown…

Mack Hill…you came through when I was at my lowest… still got that pencil…

Tracy, Cody, Jeremiah…it's tough being a Lettiere…we'll get back to that place…one day…

Alla mia famiglia e ai miei amici a casa in Costiera Amalfitana… e ad Accerra…finalmente con voi mi sento a casa…

Couldn't have done any of this without the aforementioned Warden…Craig Gore…my mentor and confidant…talk about believing in a mothafucka…

Pops…my best friend…the greatest writer I'll ever know…

…and if you think I forgot you…I didn't…

…alla mia musa ispiratrice…la mia stufalina…
La Mia Clementina…

CHAPTER 1
STRAIGHT THROUGH, WIRED

As I left the gray and dreary mid-west December for the eternal sunshine of Los Angeles I knew deep down my fate had been sealed. Yet onward I pressed, summoning every bit of hubris I had to convince myself that my subconscious was wrong. The odds stacked against me, I clung to a delusional belief that luck and agility could win out in this impulsive and insane leap of faith. A downward spiral of self-destruction was on the horizon and instead of changing course I rushed towards it with open arms. But even if I could've gotten a glimpse of how it would all end would I have turned back?

Heading south out of Chicago on I-55, the downtown skyline disappeared behind me. I passed old factories and trees rising above an industrial wasteland. By the time I hit the Tri-State overpass the city where I was born and raised was a distant memory. Many times I'd driven that stretch of highway once known as the great American road called Route 66. The 20th Century path forged to signify manifest destiny. A path to possibility and prosperity, now just billboards and truck stops for two thousand miles.

I was lost in thought when the low fuel light started blinking on the instrument panel of my Dodge Charger SRT8 just outside of St. Louis. Hours had passed in what seemed like minutes. Distracted, processing what had gone down in Chicago. Desperate scenarios raced through my head. Scaring myself, thinking about the terrible things I was willing to do to fulfill a dream.

Even with my brain on autopilot I was hyper-aware of the stretches to slow down and scan for state troopers. Driving cross-country with a hundred Norcos in my pocket and a duffel with another thousand in the trunk. Fucked up thing is all those pills weren't for selling, but for my own personal use. Over the years I'd developed a serious addiction to pharmaceuticals as well as an acute skill for avoiding law enforcement.

There was also the fact I didn't possess a driver's license, just a copy of my younger brother's. We looked enough alike and I was confident that if I handed it over to a cop I could pass as him. Not that my brother Dominic had a clean record, but he still had a valid license, mine was revoked years ago. I admitted this to him in a letter once and I'm sure he got a laugh out of it lying on his prison bunk.

I drove straight through, wired on caffeine and pills. Only pulling off the interstate for gas and Red Bulls to wash down the opiates. From Illinois to New Mexico, where I finally pulled over to sleep in my car a few hours. Over halfway to Los Angeles. The red mountains and sagebrush vivid even at night, that part of the country glowing bright red and orange. Always made my imagination run wild, whether I was fighting demons or chasing dreams. On that particular night it was a heavy dose of both as I tossed and turned in the reclined leather seat.

When I woke I just sat in my car a moment, staring out at a tumbleweed-infested parking lot of a boarded-up roadside motel. Exhausted. On the verge of a nervous breakdown. What kept me going was envisioning Jackie back in L.A., sitting on the king-sized bed in my loft, wearing one of my old t-shirts with only panties underneath. Her legs bare, back against the head-board, cigarette in one hand while scrolling through a playlist of songs on her laptop to match her mood at the moment. Maybe the Pixies, or Al Green, or the Wu-Tang Clan. I wondered if it was really possible to give her the life she deserved, turn her dreams to reality. Her dreams being pretty simple. She wanted to laugh, eat tacos, and listen to me tell stories about my old man and crazy childhood. She wanted to make love whenever and wherever.

***

A week after moving to L.A., I was in Amoeba Records on Sunset Boulevard searching through the G-bin and this fire-cracker blonde, wearing faded bell-bottoms and a white tank top, sidled up and grinned, "hey". Rifling through the records, her big bright eyes shifted from mine and quickly scanned the store for security. "Donnie Hathaway?" she said as she flashed me the album, slipped it into her oversized UCLA shoulder bag, gave me a wink and strolled out. I was struck, she had me. I let her get out the door, then bee-lined to catch her.

I spotted her blonde mane bouncing in the sunlight heading east, past the Cinerama Dome. I covered some ground, but she started running and jumped on the Number 2 bus at Vine just as the doors closed. I ran after, catching up enough to see her holding the post by the rear door. Smiling at me, head cocked to the side, as if she knew I'd chase her.

As the bus stopped at a red light, I caught up and she was still looking at me with that amazing smile. Sweat running down my forehead, I popped a Marlboro Red to my lips like I was James Dean. Feigning cool, I looked away nonchalant as I tried lighting it, but was so out of breath I couldn't. As I laughed at myself, I glanced over to see her behind the glass laughing with me. She didn't get off, but as the bus started moving she scrawled her phone number in lipstick backwards. I ran for fifty yards, making sure I got the digits right, repeating them over to myself. I took out my cell and dialed. She answered, "my name's Jackie. What's yours?"

That night we hooked up, drinking cold beers while listening to the stolen Hathaway record, finishing with us in bed listening to Tina Marie. She was from Brooklyn and was twenty-one, so I had thirteen years on her. A classic beauty who loved the classics. She wanted to be an actress and was fearless, but I think she really wanted to be the damsel in distress saved by a dangerous but righteous dude but there weren't many Bogarts left in the world.

She used to write me letters and hide little notes for me around my loft, but that eventually changed. From that first night I sensed she was hiding demons just like me. My self-destructive streak ran deep, and if I was headed for hell she's the one I'd want by my side. Maybe I was attracted to women like my mother. Maybe I was meant to go out of this world like I came in, narcotics flooding every cell in my body.

As I drove, it hit me how many people were depending on me to return from Chicago to provide them with hope. With money to make a film and validate their hard work and shared dreams. My heart raced, blood pumping with adrenaline and polluted with opioids. For the first time since Chicago I checked my phone. One missed call. The name on the call log made my stomach churn. "M Burke." Marie Burke. The rich widow of a successful Chicago Alderman and old friend of my mother's family.

By the time I was four, my mother oscillated between sobriety and month-long drug binges. Disappearing with strange men, heroin homecomings when she found her way back. She'd burned every bridge she had to high society, excommunicated from respectability, blaming my father for her shotgun wedding to a 'greasy Dago' from Back of the Yards. After my mother was gone, Marie served as a benefactor. For some reason she had a soft spot for me.

When I was fifteen, I watched my father wither away from pancreatic cancer in the dilapidated apartment we shared. Marie paid for his cremation, paid the back rent, and hooked me up with a city job painting fire hydrants. When facing expulsion from public high school for fighting, she paid for my catholic education at Mt. Carmel. Over the years, whenever I needed a loan she'd give it to me and I always paid her back. When I asked her to invest a few hundred thousand dollars in an independent film I was going to make, she said my passion was infectious and agreed without hesitation.

———

Twenty-four hours earlier I walked into Gene and Georgetti's for what I thought was a celebration of a partnership. I'd written a screenplay called "79th Street" based on a short story I wrote in Coach Antonetti's high school English class that'd been germinating in my mind for years. To everyone's surprise, it won several script contests, got me meetings with agents and a few producers promised me deals. After it all turned out to be hot air, I decided if no one else was going to put their money where their mouth was then I'd make it myself. Marie promised to back me so I moved to L.A. and put together a team of like-minds to help me produce it, spending two hundred and eighty thousand to get it off the ground. It was every dollar I had, and I'd put it all on the line.

I found Marie in a red leather corner booth dedicated to her husband, the late Alderman Burke who had held court there since the 60's. A framed picture of him on the wall over the booth. As I slid in across from her, she smiled at me, cheeks rosy from having already polished off an expensive bottle of wine.

"I can see you've been enjoying the sun out west. Got that Frank Sinatra Palm Springs tan," she said. She took a sip of pinot and added, "but you look tired. Mickey."

"It's a lotta work putting a film together," I said. The statement was true, but there were other factors affecting my state of constant exhaustion. Was hoping she thought the bags under my eyes were from late nights spent on re-writes, not from the copious amounts of pills I'd been popping to keep myself right.

She smiled and motioned to a bottle of Miller Lite she'd pre-ordered for me, "I made an educated guess."

I took a swig, "thanks. You guessed right."

"I read the script. It was definitely entertaining. Love how you painted your uncle Conrad and his cronies in such a heroic light," she said, not hiding her sarcasm.

"It's a redemption story," I explained. "Like all the best anti-heroes. You know, like Cool Hand Luke."

"Your uncle was a petty criminal who never performed a selfless act in his life. Delusions of grandeur seen through the rose-colored glasses of his nephew far as I'm concerned. But for someone without a literature degree I was impressed. Your writing is good. Raw, but poetic."

Didn't appreciate the pot shot at my uncle. He had many flaws but always treated me with kindness. But I let it go and assured her, "I'm still working on the third act, but I'll send it to you soon as I'm finished."

"It'll make for a good movie, Mickey. Some day."

"Some day? You thinkin' that's the new title?"

Marie finished her wine, signaled the waiter to bring another bottle. She sighed as she said, "it's not a good time right now, Mickey. I hate being the bearer of bad news, but we should put the movie on the back burner. Or at least my participation in it."

My stomach sank, "you gotta be joking, Marie. Your participation is the budget. What happened? Last time we talked you were all-in on this."

"Maybe you haven't been paying attention to the news gallivanting around Tinseltown, but we're on the brink of a recession. The markets are crashing, most of my portfolio along with them. My financial advisor is hoping things will stabilize in a year or two."

"A year or two? We're in pre-production, people are depending on us. We're scheduled to shoot next month."

"It's just a little movie Mickey," she said. "Put it on hold and come home for awhile. I have an empty unit in the building at 35th and Halsted. You can stay there rent free, go back to work, save up some money."

Just a little movie? It wasn't until that moment that I realized she'd never taken me serious and never planned on financing the project. Incensed, I laid it out for her, "I'm not going back up on the steel. You know, after all my surgeries I never got cleared by the doctors and if I'd gotten hurt again I'd be ass out. But I did it anyways to raise money for this fuckin' film. I put in every cent of my workmen's comp settlement. I even sold my old man's Monte Carlo, the only thing he left me that was worth a damn."

"Mickey, I know how much it meant…"

I cut her off, "I don't think you do. You promised if I put in the start-up cash you'd come in and match my money dollar for dollar and go from there, no problem. Maybe win an Oscar, or the very least use it as a tax write-off. What am I supposed to tell everyone?"

"I know what I said, but things change." She looked me over grinning, "you remind me of your father when he was young. You both got that hot Dago blood. Just forget about the film, Mickey. It was pie in the sky anyways."

Having heard enough I downed my beer, slamming it on the table as I stood. "My uncle might've just been a petty criminal, but your husband was a fuckin' leech. A fat Irish prick who lined his pockets with kickbacks paid for from the taxes of hard-working men like my father. He wasn't a great man, he was a fuckin' joke. And you should thank your lucky stars he kicked the bucket before he was indicted and you really lost it all."

Marie raised her voice to match mine, "after all I've done for you, this is how you talk to me?"

The waiter appeared holding the bottle of pinot, eyeing me as he asked, "Is everything alright Mrs. Burke?"

"Was just telling her I needed another drink," I said as I snatched the bottle from his hands. I swigged from the bottle as I walked out into the cold Chicago night, never looking back at her.

Did the math as I drove. Had about four grand to my name and was supposed to start shooting a movie in a few weeks. I'd rented a production office off Sunset, bought equipment, hired a casting director, a locations manager and had a lot of momentum. I'd also made a lot of promises to a lot of people. If there was one thing I hated, it was people breaking promises.

That's when I started reminiscing about the summer nights of my childhood, working as a busboy in my uncle's bar late into the night. Shooting pool with hoodlums. Feeding quarters into the jukebox playing song requests from wise guys. One of those characters was a bank-robber named Kelly. Thin, quiet, loved Johnnie Walker Blue. After a few glasses he'd open up and regale me with tales of extracting legal tender from financial institutions. The difference between the cash drawer, day-safe, and the vault. How handing a "stay calm and give me money" note to a teller got you less time than going in strong with a gun. How all banks put dye-packs inside stacks of twenties and how to spot the stack they were hidden in.

I absorbed Kelly's every word and noticed how every man in that bar treated him with the utmost respect. I learned bank robbers were a different breed. There was a sort of violent romance surrounding men who chose that particular line of

Federal crime. When Kelly stopped coming into the bar I asked my uncle about him, who informed me Kelly had been gunned down by the FBI coming out a credit union in Skokie.

My father said wise guys were full of shit, booze and drugs only compounding their tall tales. As crazy as his life was, my father remained sober. He never understood why people chose to numb their senses, chalking it up to human weakness. To be a weak man was a cardinal sin. He must've judged women differently, because he took my drug addict mother back countless times over the years. He was right about most of those felonious barflies, but Kelly was different. I believed every word he uttered, and who knew that decades later they might come in handy.

———

I popped a handful of Norcos, washed them down with Red Bull. My cellphone buzzed. Seeing Jackie's name on the screen caught me off guard. I stared at it for ten seconds. "Hey baby," I answered, every ounce of my being trying to veil my fucked-up state of mind.

"Hey," she said, followed by five seconds of the loudest silence I'd ever known. In those seconds my heart didn't beat. Years later, I'd reflect back on this pause as a tipping point in my life.

"What are you doing?" I asked.

"Nothin', just thinking about you." There were always these pauses that seemed to transcend words.

"Where are you?"

"Arizona."

"I miss laying next to you." As she said that I could picture her full, pouting lips utter those words and I got hard, forgetting the desperate measures I'd decided upon.

"Be back in L.A. in a cool minute, kid." I assured.

"I'll be waiting." She paused, then said, "Mick, I love you."

Fuck. It was the first time she'd ever said those words. This pronouncement, combined with the drugs coursing through my bloodstream, caused me to feel a twisted sense of excitement for the future.

But I played it cool, "see you soon baby."

I hung up, realizing I was going a hundred and thirty miles an hour, the sky revealing its first light as the sun began its ascent in my rearview. My frayed nerves calmed as what I needed to do came into focus.

CHAPTER 2
"L"

The Santa Ana winds were blowing mighty as I sped along the 110 southbound. Passing the exit for Dodger Stadium the lights of downtown L.A. appeared before me. They had lost their initial dazzle, no longer shining mystically, they were more foreboding.

My cell buzzed. The screen read "L." I answered, "yo, what's up?"

"Yo, homey! Got a one night special for ya."

"Cool. Just gettin' into the city now."

"You wann'em?"

"Always."

"Alright, meet me under tha arches n' bring a stack."

I knew him simply as "L". Could've stood for Lawrence or Lionel or Lucifer. L was a hustler who mainly peddled pills and weed in downtown L.A., operating as a solo artist as downtown wasn't territorial as far as gangs. It was every man for himself, and L was a survivor.

We met shortly after I moved into my loft downtown. I was

out walking, getting the lay of the land in my new hood in my new city. L was posted up in a doorway near Spring and Fifth. " Vicodin," was the single word he uttered as I passed, just loud enough for me to hear.

I didn't turn my head or break stride, just kept walking to a Rite-Aid on the corner. I went inside and bought a bottle of water. Exiting the store, I decided to make another pass by the doorway since by then my habit was requiring a dozen pills a day. The surgeries I had years before creating my taste for opiates. I wasn't full-blown dope-sick, but the cravings were coming on with a vengeance caused by the aches and pains in my bones. Doctors had stopped writing me scripts, so to maintain my self-medication regimen I'd been forced to buy off the street.

I was nearly out of pills and desperate. I approached the doorway, shadow from his ball cap hiding his face. I didn't make eye contact as I said, "walk with me."

He fell right in step behind me. Keeping about six feet back, both of us staring ahead, eyes scanning the street. He broke his silence, "you five-O?"

"Not a chance," I said, putting my Chicago accent on thick, letting him know I was from out of town and lessen his suspicion.

"Got five for twenty. Fifty gets you fifteen," he said as we slowed a bit.

I glanced back to get my first look at L. A black dude, late thirties, dressed in Dickies and black ball cap with no identifying logo. No flashy clothes or jewelry so not to draw attention. But he did wear a slick, tilted smirk signaling he was open for business.

"Lookin' for a bigger order," I told him.

"Can get you twenty M's right now for seventy-five."

I didn't't know what the hell 'M's' were but played along. "Alright, I'll check'em out."

"Gotcha. Meet me at the Subway 'round the corner. Grab a six-inch and I'll see ya."

In the Subway, I ordered a turkey and cheese and Pepsi and sat down at a corner table. Only a few other people were eating, but they paid me no attention. Kept my eyes on the entrance, no intention of eating. My mind was racing as I sat there and asked myself, "what had I become? Waiting for a stranger to sell me narcotics?"

Before my legs were broken in the fall I'd never ingested any drugs besides caffeine and alcohol. I'd never taken a hit off a joint. Never drank hard liquor, besides a shot here or there when celebrating a birthday or at a wake. My one vice was cheap blue-collar beer. My go-to being Miller Lite. I was a jock in my youth, spent a year in college on a baseball scholarship, then years as an iron-worker. So chugging a twelve-pack with teammates or tossing a few cold ones back after a ten-hour day climbing on the steel, drinking beer was basically a requirement. As my addiction grew my perspective changed, experiencing just how easy it was to become chemically dependent no matter how strong a man's willpower.

L came through the door and nonchalantly strolled past me without uttering a word, approaching the Asian girl at the counter who handed him a cup. He stepped to the drink dispenser, filled it with ice water, then sat down across from me and tapped my knee under the table with his fist.

"There's twenty for ya," drinking from the cup with his free hand, while he passed me a baggie of pills under the table. I took the handoff and slid them into my pocket.

I passed the folded cash into his palm, "that's seventy-five, but you offered a better price on fifteen."

"Yeah, but these 'M's'. The primo shit, no generic." He grinned, "you from New York? That accent sounds like you some Italian mobster."

"Nah, man. South side Chicago. And I definitely ain't no mobster."

"Alright, Chi. Check out them M's and call me, I can get ya anything you want." He slid a napkin towards me and headed for the door. I opened the napkin to see a phone number he'd scrawled on it, along with a big "L". When I looked up, he'd already disappeared.

Hit the James M. Woods exit south of downtown, went east to Hill, then south to a McDonald's on Washington. L's mention of 'arches' was code for the 'golden arches'. I found a table in the corner, eyes on the door. On my tray were a cheeseburger, fries, and a soda with a straw. On the side was a Miller Lite from my glove compartment. I took a swig as L slid in across from me.

"How you been my man?" I asked.

"Just livin' the dream on these streets, feel me? But check it out," he slid his cup next to mine, switched our straws and sipped from my cup. "There's five hunnert blues and somethin' special for you. Customer appreciation day."

By that point I could barely tell the difference between greens, blues, whites or 'M's.' I was popping handfuls of whatever I could get, my habit now up to thirty a day. Even though I had a bag full of pills in my trunk, I bought more whenever I could. L's super-sized cup of painkillers would add maybe two weeks to my stash.

"Good lookin' out my guy," I said, handing him ten one-hundred dollar bills folded in a napkin under the table.

"Know you're not into Oxy's, but I got this hook-up sellin' them super cheap."

"Nah, I'm good. I'm about done with these things anyway," as if saying it out loud would magically give me the strength to stop whenever I wanted.

"No doubt you got a handle on your shit," not believing me for a second. L then changed gears, "what up wit the Hollywood thing? Shoot that movie yet?"

"Just doin' a polish on the script, then it's a go."

"Hell yeah, Homey. That's what I'm talkin' 'bout! Just don't forget your friend when ya get famous."

"Never," I said.

We slapped hands and L did his disappearing act. I counted to sixty then hurried out, popping a handful of blues as I got in my car. As I hit the 101 a calm washed over me, the pills dissolving in my stomach. Convinced I was born to do something extraordinary in life, even if it meant risking my life. My only fear was leaving Jackie alone in the world. But those thoughts melted away as the opiates flooded my bloodstream.

CHAPTER 3
CROOKED SMILE

I was renting a loft downtown by Sixth and Main, high ceilings with exposed beams. The rivets were visible, the stamp of U.S. steel on each piece. The doors to the rooms were heavy wood and smoked glass. Twenty-foot arched windows looking out to the west. The building's management was having a hard time leasing units at the time, so I got a great deal. The area was beginning to gentrify, hipsters moving into the arts district. It wasn't unusual to see a Porsche pulling into the building's garage while one block away were tents on skid row.

Exiting the elevator on the top floor I was immediately hit by the smell of marijuana and the sound of music playing. I knew the smells and sounds were Jackie. I opened the door and there she was, that crooked smile across her beautiful face. Large, sexy, hazel eyes that were somewhat sedated. Standing barefoot, she was almost a foot shorter than me. A lamp lit up her long, wild, curly mane of dirty blonde hair as she jumped, wrapping her arms around my neck and her legs around my waist. My hands cupped her ass that was uncovered except for the thong of her panties. She peppered me with a thousand kisses.

Before a word was said I carried her to the couch. She

stripped off my jacket, t-shirt and belt. The taste of weed and beer on her tongue mixing with the scent of her recently washed hair was intoxicating. She eased my pants down and assumed her favorite position. I sat on the couch as she started to ride me. Within one minute she was in her moment of ecstasy, thrusting her hips into me.

"I'm coming," she said as if the words were her last gasp. She came another two times in the next minute, her eyes rolled back into their sockets, we simultaneously hit the hilt the last time. Still inside her, she collapsed into me. I wanted to die like that.

"I fuckin' missed you," Jackie said with her head buried in the crook of my shoulder, breath heavy and content.

"I fuckin' missed you too," a smile tightening my cheeks. "I'll jump in the shower real quick, and whattya say we have a beer and stare at each other a while."

She stood up, staring at me her cheeks flushed, eyes satiated. Leaned her head down cupping my cheeks in both hands, "I want to hear about Chicago. I want you to tell me a story. God I'm so happy to see you," as she planted another kiss upon my lips.

I walked across the concrete floor barefoot and naked, opened the fridge, cracked open a Lite. Glancing back toward the living room, she looked like a lioness smoking a cigarette. Finished the beer in one long thirsty pull, then grabbed another for the shower. Body was exhausted, my mind was racing. Thought about what I'd tell Jackie, the truth as it stood that second? Or the truth I was about to create from sheer willpower?

Showered and shaved, felt like a new man after all those hours on the road. Put on a fresh pair of jeans, Adidas, and a Dago-T. Walked back to the living room and Jackie was on the couch, wearing my frayed White Sox T-shirt, drinking a Lite and listening to the Red Hot Chili Peppers.

"How's classes goin'?" I asked.

"Philosophy is pretty rad. We've been discussing a book that's got you on my mind all week. 'Thus Spoke Zarathustra'."

"Good ol' Nietzsche, huh?"

She nodded, "you're too much a dreamer to be an existential-ist. You'd never accept a fate you at least had some hand in."

Jackie's dad was a writer and mom a poet back in Brooklyn. She was going to UCLA for Philosophy and Art. A hot hippie chick, brilliant and articulate. Unlike most men, I'd always taken her serious as we conversed about the human condition. It was the sexiest thing in the world to me. Jackie kissed me hard, then reached past me to grab two cigarettes. She lit them both, put one in my mouth.

"Such a dark perspective on such a happy-go-lucky fool as me. You see me as the Superman? Always fancied myself more like Spiderman, climbing buildings and whatnot."

She got serious, "you've already been through a lot in life, Mick."

I looked at her as I paraphrased Nietzsche. "If only I could be the master of myself, have the ultimate self-control so as to not be tempted by such seduction as a utopian existence that is my imagination. You sprawled out naked on my bed, surrounded by sustenance to last us a lifetime. We could live forever in pure bliss."

"I'll never catch up to you," Jackie said, amazed yet annoyed with my knowledge. She picked up a joint, lit it, took a pull and handed it over. "How was Chicago? She really give you the money?"

Before I answered I took a pull. THC mixing with the pills, the edge taken off my wide-eyed buzz as I became more chill. Affording me a temporary reprieve from the guilt I felt as I started weaving lies. "Yeah, Marie gave me the go-ahead. Like she promised."

Jackie asked, "you fuck her for it?"

I could only grin, "you're cute when you're jealous."

"Wasn't she what you called your benefactor?"

"She was," I admitted. "But I got somethin' new."

"Yeah, what's that?" Jackie asked.

"A muse…that I'm in love with."

Jackie about burst into tears as I picked her off the couch and carried her upstairs to bed. We made love again, this time slowly and gently. We fell asleep in each other's arms. I did not dream that night.

CHAPTER 4
FILL IT WIT CASH

I woke up before Jackie, chased a handful of Norcos with Red Bull. Left Jackie a note on the bathroom sink telling her to have a beautiful day and I'd see her later. Pulling out of the garage on Main at 6:30 am, the streets were just beginning to show signs of life.

I headed north to Pasadena and hit the 210. Running through certain locations, easy access to freeways, affluent neighborhoods. Working solo and not strapped, was looking for small banks in wealthy areas that typically didn't have armed security. At that point I wasn't too familiar with L.A. besides downtown and Hollywood, which in my mind were already off-limits. Too congested with traffic and bystanders. And as a filmmaker weeks away from principal photography I considered it bad luck to shit where I ate.

My SRT8 had a navigation screen but I didn't know or care how to use it. Kept a Rand-McNally Road Atlas under the passenger seat to reference if I ever lost my way. I was analog. Jackie found it sexy I could study a map for thirty seconds then remember how to get somewhere across town. Pulled over at a gas station in Pasadena and consulted the atlas. Got to admit, I didn't do a lot of research when I started my crime spree.

Heading east I would exit every few miles, venture off the expressway a few blocks in either direction, then jump back on the 210. Monrovia, Duarte, Azusa, Arcadia. All the way out to Rancho Cucamonga, where I exited and pulled into a shopping center parking lot, casing a California Teachers Credit Union.

Checked my phone and there was a text from Jackie. "Off to class. See you later. Let's get Chinese. Your note was so sweet! LUV U Mickey!"

....

In a Big 5 Sporting Goods I bought a backpack, a pair of batting gloves, aviator sunglasses and a neoprene ski mask. The first of many shopping trips I'd make at Big 5 over the next few months, always paying cash for gear and disguises. I climbed into my ride, popped a handful of blues, and decided against the Credit Union.   Dead-set on raising the million dollars I'd promised I jumped on the 210 heading west.

Exited in San Dimas, which I'd initially passed since it was the setting for "Bill and Ted's Excellent Adventure." Cracked myself up as I pulled off the freeway, quoting from the ridiculous time-travel comedy.   "San Dimas High School football rules!"

As I came to a red light, a Sheriff's Deputy cruiser was in the turning lane to my left. A CHP Officer was opposite in the right turning lane. Eyed both in my periphery without moving my head. Both the Deputy and Trooper stared over at me as I calmly stared straight ahead.   Then both looked away as our lights turned green and we went our separate ways. To me that meant San Dimas was a good omen.

————

Five minutes later I spotted a Bank of America in a shopping plaza that looked prime. At the south end of the plaza, a tree-lined side street running perpendicular. I drove past several times, casing the best getaway route and best place to leave my ride running out of sight.

Realizing I was using my own car I felt like a fool, until I noticed there were no windows on three-sides of the bank. Hated starting off as a cowboy, diving into a life of crime with more balls than planning, but the Norcos coursing through my blood insisted on blessing me for this mission. Pulled over and parked fifty yards from the B of A. Put on my gear from Big 5, climbed out leaving the engine running and door ajar.

The mask, gloves, empty backpack were a combined two pounds but felt like the weight of the world as I took the last three strides to the door and entered the bank. Only one middle-aged female teller at the counter finishing up with a customer, who was trading hundreds for a bank bag full of rolls of quarters for a coin-operated business. In a corner office, a male manager rifled through a cabinet.

As I approached the teller sporting a neoprene ski mask and batting gloves I saw her face drop from bright and sunny, to sheer terror, then bounce back to smiling and cheerful as if knowing it was the best way to survive. I held out the duffel I usually used for carrying drugs, "fill it with cash. Hands where I can see 'em. Eyes on me." Scared, she complied. "Twenties and higher. No dye-packs. Hear what I'm sayin', sweetheart?"

Only took her seconds to empty the cash from her drawer into the backpack, tearing the bands off each stack of ones, tens and twenties as she tossed the wads into the duffel. Not having asked her to do that, I took note of this courtesy for future robberies. I glanced to the manager, still rifling with files in the office, completely unaware his branch was being ripped off. I looked back at the teller, holding her hands palms out, resting her elbows on the counter as she kept smiling in full submission.

Pushed open the door, peeled off the mask, strode past the ATM's where a customer depositing a check paid me no mind. Soon as I turned the corner I broke into a sprint and within five seconds was throwing my car into drive. My adrenaline was jacked but I had the presence of mind not to stomp the gas and draw attention with those Hemi tailpipes. Slowly eased it into 1st and waved to an old lady who crossed in front of me holding a bouquet of fresh flowers. I wondered if they were for a funeral or graduation or a dinner party as I pulled out of the plaza and made it to the freeway in less than a minute.

It wasn't until I merged onto the 210 and realized none of the cash in my duffel was going to explode that I took a long, hard breath. No sirens. No chase. No helicopters overhead. Eyed the rearview, the fact I'd just robbed a bank sinking in. Remember the radio was playing Audioslave's "Shadow on the Sun."

Too excited to wait I used my knees to steer as I flipped through the bills. Mostly twenties, fifties, some loose hundreds. No dye-packs or GPS tracking chips. I'd made ten thousand, three hundred and sixty dollars in just thirty seconds. On one hand it seemed so easy making ten G in such a short amount of time, on the other hand I'd have to hit fifty banks to raise the money I needed.

CHAPTER 5
ROOFTOP

Exhaustion flooded my body as I pulled into the garage of my building. Grabbed the backpack and Rand-McNally Atlas. Stepped to the elevator and there I was greeted by a face that both comforted and horrified me. Timothy Flanagan, the nuts and bolts of "79th Street."

"Yo, Mickey!" Timmy exclaimed in a thick South Boston accent. "We gettin' this big production going or what?"

"What's up, kid?" I pressed the button for my loft, trying to churn criminal adrenaline into some semblance of a creative discussion. "Ya read the latest draft?"

"Fuckin'-A, Mickey. Fuckin' great! That chick give you the dough we needed?"

"We're good, just workin' out specifics," I lied.

"Fuckin'-A! Been stealin' from Peter to pay Paul just to eat," Timmy said, a desperation in his eyes that I felt responsible for.

He rode the elevator to the top with me even though he lived on the fourth floor. I looked to him, "gotta make a couple calls. Meet ya on the roof?"

"Fuckin'-A I'll be holdin' court."

As the door opened to my loft I assured him, "I'll bring some beers and we'll nail down the start-date."

I entered the loft, thinking of my father and of his favorite Hemingway quote. "Courage is grace under fire." Which basically translated to 'just be cool' when dealing with the pressures of the world crushing down on you. To me courage and loyalty were the two most important traits that family, friends or lovers had to possess to gain entry and remain in my life. More than a few times being too courageous or too loyal would come back to haunt me, but I never regretted holding myself to high standards even when others couldn't.

I locked the deadbolt behind me. Stepped to the kitchen sink and splashed water on my face. Unzipped the backpack and quickly recounted the cash from the B of A. Took the few-thousand of my own from a coffee can in the cabinet. Tossed my various bags of opiates next to the money. I stared down at the counter, realizing my life boiled down to less than fifteen grand and twelve hundred pills. A handful of Norcos quickly stopped this dilemma from overwhelming me, as I threw on some shorts and grabbed a 12-pack of Lites.

Most of the people in the building didn't have nine-to-five jobs, most aspiring to be in the 'industry.' Actors. Models. Musicians. Fashionistas. Which meant most of them spent their days lounging around the rooftop pool. I found Timmy reading a copy of *Variety* in a chair admiring two beautiful, young girls sunning themselves a few yards away. Timmy was 25 but looked 18. Five-eight, cherubic, charming as fuck. A tough kid from South Boston, always talking through the side of his mouth with twinkling Irish eyes. A hustler with big dreams who'd won the L.A. Film Festival for best short the year before, a semi-true story that chronicled his criminal older brothers who ran a sportsbook operation.

When I saw it I had to meet him. We hit it off like we'd been separated at birth. Instead of attending the snooty-ass festival after-party in Santa Monica we got drunk on whiskey at HMS Bounty, a dive on Wilshire, and by sunrise I'd hired him to direct his first feature film.

Handed Timmy a beer as I sat beside him, "ready to shake things up, kid?"

He cracked the beer and took a swig, "so you secured the financing?"

"Yeah, kid, we're good. The old lady's gonna move some things around so we'll get the money in chunks. Plus I got meetings with a few other possible investors. You don't worry about the dough, I need you focused on the talent and that gritty vision you put up on that screen." Referring to his earlier comment about rent I asked, "ya need some scratch, kid?"

"You've been on time with everything and I didn't want to ask…"

"Say no more." I handed him two grand. "That'll cover your nut this month?"

"Yeah Mickey, thanks."

"So what happened to our producers?"

"When the cash didn't hit Escrow quick enough they bailed. But I say fuck those college boys, we can produce this movie ourselves."

I nodded, "got our leads bein' cast. We bought a Red Camera. Got two equipment trucks secured for two months. We're doin' this my brother."

Timmy's eyes went wide. "Fuck yeah, can't wait."

"But you gotta know there's no going over-budget on this. Hear me, kid?"

"I hear ya, Mickey." He clinked beer cans with me, excited. "We're gonna do this and take this town by storm!"

His excitement infectious, I decided, "why don't you round up the players and let's have a pre-production meeting at the office."

"Got it, I'll start making calls. You gonna bring Jackie?"

"If she doesn't have class."

"Oh she can ditch for the '79th Street' jump-off!   Plus, I promised I'd find a part for her in the film," he said.

I smiled. "Smart man."

I stood and turned to the bathing beauties nearby, "you girls should get to know this guy here. He's about to be a big-time director."

One of them scoffed, "really?"

I nodded, "not kiddin'. If I was you I'd get in on the ground floor." As I walked away both beauties moved closer to where Timmy was sitting, looking at him like maybe he was some-body. I'd definitely made that motherfuckers' day.

Back in the loft I cracked more Lites as I went to work on my plan. Using a notebook, different colored pens and my Atlas I made a bank-robbery map and manifesto. My hand couldn't write fast enough to keep up with my thoughts, which at the time seemed fool-proof as I popped opiates and told myself my old man would've done the same if he'd found himself in such a dire situation. Also tried convincing myself if I pulled it off my father would be proud I beat the system regardless of my growing narcotics addiction.

Knew I'd gotten lucky on my first attempt in more ways than one. Also knew teller-drawers typically only held five to ten grand at most. Needed to go after auxiliary-drawers and day-safes, which contained enough cash to refill teller drawers through the day without employees having to go into the vault. Hitting a bank vault could net six-figures but was on another level, requiring an armed crew willing to shoot it out with the cops.

I was working alone, targeting suburban branches and hoping day-safes would serve my purpose. Had no doubt I could get forty or fifty per bank if I did it right, but I needed to procure "G-rides" going forward. Nondescript. Reliable. Fast. I had a connect.

CHAPTER 6
GATO

F irst time in L.A. I'd driven out my prized possession. My father's '70 Monte Carlo. Under 20,000 miles. Original champagne paint. Mint-condition. No rust even though it was a Mid-west car because my father refused to drive it in the snow. Blue Book listed for 30K. The only thing my mother never swindled from him and the only inheritance there was to leave. Got looks from O.G.'s, girls, collectors who'd offered me twice what it was worth but I always swore I'd never sell it.

One night cruising back from Redondo Beach on the 110 North the transmission started bucking and I ended up on the side of the freeway in South Central at midnight. The Mexican tow-truck driver got me to his garage at 47th and Central and told me it'd be a few days until the Monte Carlo could be looked at. Or he could call his cousin Gato, who'd come over and check it out no matter what time of night. Being a white dude, alone, not strapped, with a classic ride in the middle of the hood was not a good feeling as the tow-truck driver kept glancing at me while speaking Spanish to some dude on the other end.

Half-hour later I started to regret agreeing to meet "Gato" as four vato bangers appeared at the garage, serious gang ink, eye-fucking me with guns in their waistbands.

"That is one sweet ride homes," Gato said, admiring my Monte Carlo as he slapped hands with the tow-truck driver. Tried sizing him up, figuring it was some kind of trap as I scanned the garage for the nearest tool I could grab up to use as a weapon. He then held out his hand for me to slap, "what up fool, they call me Gato. How'd your white ass end up down here this late at night? Ya like Latin pussy, huh?"

Shook my head, "nah. The transmission."

Gato and his vatos eyed me hard, then suddenly busted out laughing. "Calm down fool, we ain't gonna rob you!" Gato pointed to the tow-truck driver, "just pay mi primo a hundred for the tow and I got it from here."

I gave his cousin a C-note and ended up hanging with Gato and his vatos until the sun came up. He went to work on the Monte Carlo's transmission as him and his boys shared blunts and we finished off a case of Tecate. Apprehensive at first, we became fast friends, Gato and the bangers having met few white dudes like me who were comfortable on their turf. When I told them about the car's legacy and how my old man bought it new off the lot on Western Avenue, Gato and his boys dug the fact I was still cruising it in his honor.

Gato only charged me three bills for a job that would've cost a G at any other garage. Like most guys he fell in love with the old man's treasure and made me promise if I ever decided to sell he got first dibs. From that night on a kinship was formed. And when I got desperate enough to sell the Monte Carlo, I gave it to him for a steal at twenty grand.

....

Gato lived in South L.A. with his girlfriend, their three kids, and his *abuela* who was about eighty-five, blind and didn't speak a word of English. All six of them lived in a sun-bleached, two-bedroom house with three pit bulls chained up in the backyard that constantly barked at their growing brood of cats. Parked in the alley along the fence and peeked over the gate. Gato was beneath an old Lincoln working his magic.

"Yo, Gato!" I called out. "What's good, dog?"

He slid from under the Lincoln with a big smile on his face, "Mr. Hollywood. What's up, fool?" He opened the gate and we slapped hands, "step into my office. I'll grab some beers."

I was buzzed from downing a dozen Lites and wired from the pills, a little nervous about initiating the conversation. "Sounds good, kid. But I can't stay long and was already drinkin' by the pool today."

"Sounds like a tough life," Gato joked as he wiped grease from his face and grabbed two Tecates from a cooler. He gave me one and we cracked them open, "salud."

We bumped cans, "I got a favor to ask."

Reading my face, Gato glanced around to make sure no one was within earshot. "Talk to me, homes."

"I need a G-ride. Maybe more than one. That somethin' you can handle?"

"I got you, fool. What's goin' on?"

"Better you don't know."

"You're right," he agreed. "Just gimme an hour or two heads up and I got you. What model you lookin' for?"

"Low-key. Dependable. And fast. I'm willin' to pay a G a piece."

"You got it, homes, but check it, you pay the going rate. Three bills. You pay anything more than that? It's disrespect." Gato then thought, and asked, "what happened to this fuckin' movie you're makin'?"

"It's still a go. Just gotta tie up some loose ends."

As I went to leave Gato reached out, "yo whiteboy, sure you don't want another beer? I'll have *abuela* whip up some of her famous cataract tacos."

Shook my head, "next time."

CHAPTER 7
XANAX

Several nights a week Jackie bartended at this tourist joint on Third Street Promenade in Santa Monica. When I got back to the loft and saw she wasn't home yet, I texted her to say I'd pick her up at 11PM after her shift. Then to add to the mix of alcohol and opiates roiling inside my body I decided to pop a couple of Jackie's Xanax.

Before I'd met her she suffered severe panic attacks, so was prescribed them and would sometimes take half of one when she couldn't sleep. Leading up to my Chicago trip I'd depleted all the Xanax she'd stored up. Over fifty in a few weeks. Telling her I couldn't sleep due to stressing over the film, but mainly I found Xanax countered the negative effects of all the blues I was popping. Jackie never asked questions and like a good girl had gotten a refill while I was away.

I laid down on the couch, my heart feeling like it was going to burst through my chest. Didn't think it possible I could ever fall asleep, but after five minutes the Xanax kicked in and pulled me into darkness as the warm night air mixed with the sounds of the downtown streets below drifting in through the open windows.

When I woke it was 2AM and there was Jackie sitting cross-legged on the couch staring at the TV. No music. No sexy smile. Not happy. I stared at her as she pretended to be oblivious to my presence, "baby, I'm sorry. Had my phone on vibrate. Was gonna come up to the bar early and have a drink 'til you got off."

Jackie glared at me, dragging on a cigarette as she tried calming down, "how many Xannies did you take? And you mixed them with booze? Are you trying to kill yourself, Mickey?"

"Just popped a few and a coupla beers to help me sleep, that's all." I stood and went into the kitchen and poured a glass of water. My back to Jackie, "did you eat?"

Jackie scoffed, "you didn't answer the phone? Didn't return my texts? No I didn't eat! I took a cab home, thinking crazy thoughts…"

I cut her off, "come on baby, I was tired, that's all." I walked over and sat next to her. Her eyes wide and truly sad. My heart melted as I put my arms around her. She did not relent. "Really baby, I'm sorry."

"I opened the door to see you passed out on the couch. I was afraid to come near you, thinking you had died…" she had tears coming down her cheeks. She was shaken as she pulled away from me, "fuck Mickey. You can't be taking Xanax and drinking! I know you think you're invincible…"

"Relax, kid. Come here," I held my arms out and she finally embraced me. "Are you hungry?"

"Not really, but I know you are. You seem to keep coming back to it," a smile working its way to her face.

I stood up smiling down at her, "I'll take a shower and you decide what you want to do. I'll know your decision when I come out of the bathroom. Deal?"

While I was in the shower Jackie smoked a fresh bowl and cooked a frozen pizza. We made love and watched TV until sunrise. For a little while I'd convinced her I wasn't trying to kill myself or hurt her. But I think by then we both knew that wasn't true. As soon as she fell asleep I quietly put on my jeans, popped a handful of Norcos, and left her to dream.

CHAPTER 8
WHISKEY FROM VENICE

G ot on the 101 North heading towards the Valley. Exited the 118 a few miles west of the 405. A feeling of paranoia settled in soon as I hit the intersection and realized there were banks on all four corners. When the light turned green I went straight for a mile, then doubled-back to case new opportunities.

Above the intersection was a steep hill with middle-class homes and no main streets. A block away was a shuttered self-serve carwash, overrun with weeds and broken glass. Perfect spot to leave a getaway car idling. Very little foot traffic and no other businesses would have a clear line of sight if I parked there. The Chase Bank at the northern most corner was part of a strip mall. The other three banks, Wells Fargo, Bank of California, and Sunset Credit Union, were stand-alone buildings spread out on the other corners. Two blocks from the expressway with only one stoplight between the car wash and entrance ramp.

The Chase was closest to the abandoned carwash. The corner store was a mailbox type place that only had one employee working during the day. Other side of the Chase was a pet groomer and a tanning salon. Got out and walked past the front door of the bank on the way to the mailbox store. Could only see my reflection as the windows had mirrored tint. Entered the store and saw a rolling door shut at the service desk, no cameras, banks of P.O. boxes on each wall. Opened my phone and pretended to read text messages as I did another pass by the bank. Perfect timing as an old lady exited and I got a look inside, glimpsing what appeared to be a small office with two female tellers behind the counter. Decided that would be my next bank.

....

Hit a resale shop on Hollywood Boulevard specializing in old wardrobes and props donated from film and TV sets. After dropping four bills I could've outfitted a whole line-up of different government employees. Postal workers, utility workers, police uniform complete with badge, radio and nightstick. Three different wigs, a couple mustaches and a beard.

Headed west through Hollywood and kept going until I was in Venice, scenarios playing out in my head as I drove. Everything from entering banks with various disguises to outrunning the cops on the way to Mexico played in my imagination with Mickey Fortunato as the star.

I parked, popped a handful of pills and walked the boardwalk. Stopped at several bars and bodegas, grabbing a beer and pounding them at every spot. Strolled for a few hours until the afternoon sun turned to a fading kaleidoscope of dull amber. I was numb to stress as I sat down in the sand staring out across the Pacific. I checked my phone. Jackie had not called or texted. Watching the waves roll up onto the sand and fizzle to nothing I questioned whether I'd be able to live with myself if things went south and I went to prison. My mind was made up, I wouldn't allow the law to capture me alive. Being pragmatic was not in the cards for me, if it ever was.

As I walked back to my car I bought a pint of cheap whiskey and started polishing it off. Like I said, I almost never drank hard liquor but it didn't feel like it was me making decisions anymore, but rather a puppet master pulling my strings from on high.

I took Pico all the way back downtown. Watching the neighborhoods change from Westwood to Alvarado showed the strange dichotomy that is Los Angeles. From the wealthy to the downtrodden, such a short distance on the street but a galaxy apart in the eyes of the socially and economic elite. When I reached Alvarado I phoned Gato.

"Talk to me homes."

"Need a ride for tomorrow."

"What time?"

"Ten o'clock and I'll throw in another hundred if you can have it delivered."

"Got you, fool. And it's three bills. Just let me know where."

"Alright, hit you back."

As I hung up I felt invincible from the drugs and the booze and my ever-growing bravado. Pulled off Pico just before passing under the Harbor Freeway and studied my Atlas. Then I called Gato back and he immediately answered, "my homey will meet you at ten anywhere you want. He's already got the rims."

"Sheldon Arleta Park," I told him. "Between the five and one-seventy freeways. Tell him to look for my Charger." Soon as I said this I realized his homey could potentially be a witness, but I calculated it wouldn't ever come to that if he was one of Gato's guys who helped him rip G-rides.

"I got it homey. Hey man," he paused for a few seconds.

"You're a good dude, don't wanna see you get in a wreck out there."

"I'm all good all day, Gato."

As I hung up I got an incoming call from Timmy.

"What's up, kid," I answered.

"Yo, Mickey. I called the cast and crew. The girl that's gonna play Conrad's side piece and our grip slash ELT slash gaffer slash assistant to everything, not sure she can make it to the pre-production party, slash meeting, if we do it tomorrow," he said, trying to sound like a pro.

"Does it gotta be tomorrow?" I asked, knowing my day was going to be action packed.

"If we wait, we'll lose Detective O'Brien and the kid playing Conrad's nephew for two weeks. They're main cast."

"Tim, if it's gotta be tomorrow then let's do it," I said, the whiskey from Venice was hitting me in a bad way. "But the later the better. I got a couple important things to do in the morning."

"I told everyone to be at the office at three. That gonna work, bossman?"

I clocked my day. G-ride at ten, bank at eleven, switch cars by eleven thirty, back at the loft by noon. It didn't leave much time to gather myself. "Fuck, I just remembered. Jackie's got a two o'clock class tomorrow that she can't skip," I said, Timmy finished my sentence.

"She's got a test, I know. I ran into her a little bit ago in the lobby. She said she'll be done in forty-five minutes, tops. I'll scoop her from school if you can grab the provisions and set the party up." He paused as I tried to process my day. "If that's cool with you?"

"Yeah. See ya tomorrow, kid."

"Hey Mick."

"What's up?"

"Here we go mothafucka!" He said and hung up.

Yeah, if he only knew.

CHAPTER 9
BE THERE IN 45

arrived back at the loft exhausted and overwhelmed, thinking about my workload the next day. Jackie had night class, so I figured I'd at least have the place to myself for a few hours. But when the elevator doors opened, there she was. Jackie looked just as surprised to see me as I was her, both of us with guilty looks on our faces.

"Thought you had class?" I hugged her and she gave me a tentative embrace in return.

"Called my professor, told him I wasn't feeling well," she sounded stoned out of her mind.

"You alright?" I asked, getting a closer look at her. Her eyes veered away as she dropped her hands to mine.

"Yeah, I'm good. I just wanted to buy some time, ya know?"

Those words sent a weakness to my knees. *"Buy time?"*

"I need to cram for this test tomorrow and per usual, I put everything off 'til the last minute. I get overwhelmed, you know..."

"Yeah, I know. I was the same way in school." Wasn't until then I noticed the bags at her feet and that she'd been waiting for the penthouse elevator. Hoping to leave before I got home.

"I'm gonna crash by Liana's house tonight," she told me.

"She's going out with some guy, told me she won't be home 'til tomorrow. Can do my cramming without distracting you and vice versa."

I sensed something was off. I wanted to beg her to stay and cuddle up next to me on the couch and share with me the latest thing she was reading in philosophy class. Instead I said, "alright. Need a ride?"

"No, I'm fine. You look exhausted, and I get my best reading done on the bus anyways."

"Yeah, guess you do."

She picked up her bags and forced a smile, "hey, I saw Tim. He's gonna pick me up from class. When were you gonna tell me about the party?"

"It's not really a party, it's a production thing..."

"Well it's gonna be great," her eyes were searching mine. "Mick, go inside. Relax. Drink some beer in the shower and get ready for tomorrow."

I pulled her in tight this time, cupped her ass and we came face to face. "You good, kid?"

Her eyes bloodshot, she nodded and kissed me on the way out. "I'm good. Go, I'll see you tomorrow."

———

Tried smoking some of Jackie's weed to get to sleep but it made my mind race even more. When that didn't work I chewed a couple Xanax. After staring at the ceiling until six in the morning I finally gave up on sleep. Crawled out of my empty bed and got dressed and decided to wire myself with caffeine and painkillers to get ready for game time.

Left to pick up my G-ride at eight, figuring I'd get to the park early and scope it out. The park was empty except for a home-less guy curled up on the bare dirt under a Cypress tree. It was a small park with a run-down field house at one end, a basketball court sans rims at the other end. Parked my car along the court, using a large tree's branches as cover from the street. As I waited, I fought the urge to send a text to Jackie. Not even knowing what, just knowing I wanted to say something. I was jittery from the chemicals, but oddly calm about the job. Decided to power down my phone and focus on the task at hand.

At ten on the button a dark green Lexus pulled past and parked on the same side as me. Immediately after that a Ford F150 with tinted windows and custom rims parked in front of the Lexus. A tall Latino with a shaved head, full of tats, dressed in classic cholo garb exited the Lexus, walked around to my passenger side and knocked on the window. I rolled it down as he squatted, "you Gato's *carnal*, right?"

Recognized him from the night I'd met Gato. He was one of the bangers that helped us push my Monte Carlo into the garage. "Yeah man, hop in."

As he got in the car I placed three hundred dollar bills folded in half on the armrest. He looked at me as we shook hands, "aw shit, I remember you fool, you had that Monte with the stripes." His face lit up with a toothy smile, showing off two gold caps on top and two missing teeth on bottom, the number "13" tattooed on his lower gums where his teeth used to be. Without looking down he swiped the cash and left a key in its place.

"Check it out homey, got you a sick ass ride. A GS430," he said, a little too excited for my comfort. "If you gonna hit a lick with this ride and you appreciate my taste then let's talk in the future."

I stared straight ahead, "we'll see man. Don't know what Gato told you…"

"He said low-key and dependable. That's all dog."

I gave him a blank stare, "we'll see man."

"They call me Spantos fool. Means scarecrow."

He climbed out and got into the F150. Waited for Spantos and his ride to disappear from sight, then grabbed the backpack from my trunk and switched to the Lexus. The G-ride's steering column was stripped, hanging from a bundle of wires was an extra ignition separate from the factory unit still intact.   An amateur job, but when I tried the key in the dangling switch the car started right up.   The ride was lightning fast and quiet and hugged the road, and most importantly was a yuppie sedan that blended in with traffic.

Within fifteen minutes I was parked behind the abandoned car wash near the Chase bank.   I opened the backpack, pulled out my Atlas.   Grabbed a blonde wig with a long ponytail and pulled it snug on my head.   Followed by a shaggy mustache. Then oversized aviators.   Slid the batting gloves into the pocket of the elastic waistband cargo pants I was wearing over a pair of shorts.

I climbed from the Lexus, leaving the engine running and door ajar.   Carrying the backpack, I started towards the bank as I ran down a checklist in my head.   Tried to act natural as if I made that walk every day, as if I was just going to clock in for my shift at McDonalds.   When I rounded the corner of the strip mall there was one person entering the mailbox store, and two young women exiting the tanning salon.   As they walked my way, I pulled out my cell and pretended to scroll through text messages.   They passed without giving me a second glance.   I slid on the gloves as I approached the bank.   The reflection in the mirror-tint front doors reminded me of a character in a 70's cop show and for a split second I almost laughed at myself.

Inside the Chase, there was a counter with three tellers.   Two female, early twenties, a blonde and brunette.   One male, also early twenties.

"Good afternoon sir, how can we help you today?" he asked. Seeing the two women were busy on their teller screens, I stepped immediately to the male teller.   He was effeminate and professional.   I put the bag on the counter and kept my head cocked downward so to not allow the security cameras a clear view of my disguised face.

"You can put your hands on the counter where I can see them and keep your eyes on me," I ordered in a hushed and calm voice. "This is a robbery. I want you to open that drawer and fill this bag with large bills, twenties and above. Tear off all the bands and leave the funny money and tracers in the drawer." Before I finished giving him these instructions he was already complying, emptying the drawer as I continued. "Now I want you to walk to the next teller and repeat to her what I just told you. And remember, hands where I can see 'em."

He walked three strides over to the blonde and began speaking. She froze and the teller next to her was staring at me, also frozen. So I hopped the counter. In the middle of my leap I realized it had an employee entrance and my dumb ass could've just fucking walked around the counter instead of playing cowboy. But it was only my second bank and I chalked it up to the learning process. I grabbed the bag from the male teller and filled it with cash from the second drawer. All three tellers backed away and stood erect against the wall, giving me a wide berth as I hit the third drawer. That's when a statuesque woman appeared in the doorway to my right and we both froze. Assuming she was the manager, she held several bundles of cash in her hand. Saw her eyes dart downward and to the right and my eyes followed hers. There was a safe tucked beneath the countertop, the door was slightly ajar. A symphony began to play in my head.

I squared my body to face her and to my surprise she extended the cash out to me, not appearing the least bit nervous. As I removed the bands from the stacks she did something I'll never forget. She said, "excuse me sir" with a polite smile, stepped past me and opened the door to the safe as if I was its rightful owner. Inside were more stacks of cash that I stuffed in my pockets without tearing off the bands. So excited about grabbing the money in the safe, I momentarily forgot my own rules and once again needlessly jumped over the counter and rushed the doors. A swath of sunshine flooded the bank as I glanced back at the tellers and manager, standing in the exact same spots as I'd left them as if playing a game of freeze tag on the playground. I remember the male teller seemed shook-up, while all the women had strange smiles plastered across their faces.

Can't remember if I walked or ran to the Lexus, but soon as I jumped in I ripped off the fake mustache and batting gloves and hit the gas hard, recklessly speeding onto the street without looking. Luckily I didn't sideswipe any oncoming cars and after a few breaths I composed myself enough to not run the red light at the intersection. Those fifteen seconds seemed like an eternity as I sat there, hands about to snap the steering wheel in half. A mini-van pulled up beside me, a suburban mom who'd probably just dropped off her kids looked over at me and smiled. As I forced a smile back, I realized I was still wearing that stupid fucking wig and hoped like hell she couldn't see through my charade and see the real me.

When the light turned green I was careful not to punch it and let the mini-van get ahead of me. But soon as I saw the freeway on-ramp I hit the gas, tearing off the wig and aviators. I didn't look at the backpack, just concentrated on driving, blending into traffic. I didn't switch lanes or do any aggressive passing. My eyes constantly scanned all three mirrors as I kept my head straight ahead, trying not to think about the cash as hundreds and fifties danced through my head. I envisioned Timmy shooting the final scene of "79th Street", where a character based on my uncle Conrad was supposed to climb into an unattended cop car to make his getaway from a robbery. The character lighting up a smoke, laughing at the irony that he just might pull it off as the screen cuts to black the audience's suspicion is never confirmed.

Then I spotted a midnight blue car weaving through traffic a half-mile back coming up on me fast. Judging by its maneuvers and make, my instincts screamed unmarked car. I stomped on the gas and took the Lexus from sixty to over a hundred in seconds, carving through traffic. When the midnight blue car sped up and kept on my tail, I had no doubt it was the police. At a hundred and twenty miles an hour, I finally started pulling away from the unmarked squad just as I was nearing the 170/Hollywood split exit where I'd left my Charger SRT8.

At the last second I decided to keep going and cut across multiple lanes onto the 5 North, running the needle up the speedometer until the factory-installed governor kicked in and the STR8 maxed out at one-sixty. Depression washed over me as I passed the exit for Laurel Canyon, all the other cars on the road appearing to stand still as my life flashed before me at warp speed. For a moment I even had an out of body experience, me riding shotgun as I looked over at the drug-addict maniac behind the wheel next to me who was running from the cops towards oblivion.

The unmarked car disappeared in my rearview, but if they were onto me I knew air support was soon to follow and get on top of me any second. Knowing police choppers couldn't enter the airspace around airports, I headed for Bob Hope. There I could ditch the G-ride in a parking garage and disappear into the crowd of travelers, backpack over my shoulder like I'd just arrived on a flight and jump into a taxi. Thought it'd even make for a good scene for the movie. Timmy could shoot it gorilla style.

As I approached the exit there was a queue of cars on the ramp backed up twenty-deep, but the shoulder looked clear. I slowed to under triple digits for the first time in miles, the Lexus' engine sighing in relief as my own blood pressure red-lined. I threaded the needle between the cars creeping down the ramp and the concrete barricade, my desperado's luck continuing as the light at the bottom of the ramp turned green just in time for me to blow past the others.

I braked hard at the intersection and veered right, almost going up on two wheels and barely avoiding a collision with a

Ryder truck. The street in front of me was open so I gunned it for several blocks until I neared an overpass for San Fernando Boulevard and slowed to read the airport signage. There were multiple signs filled with terminal and airline information that I couldn't make out fast enough, so I scrapped the Bob Hope plan and kept driving beneath the overpass where I saw a sign for San Fernando. I hit the ramp, not knowing the area, but calculating that if I took San Fernando North I'd be heading back towards my Charger that was four or five miles in the opposite direction.

Was relieved when I caught a green light and swung a left as I grabbed the Atlas from under the seat. Steered with my thigh, flipping through pages until I found the right section. I was closer to the park than I thought, but realized I was trapped in a gauntlet for more than a mile, train tracks running parallel to my right, the outer fence of the airport to my left. That's when I noticed a chopper in the sky to the northwest heading towards me. I put the pedal to the metal, finally reaching the end of the airport fence and hung the first left I could. Sped a couple blocks on a pothole-riddled industrial road that turned into a residential street, then parked along the curb near a corner, a large tree giving me cover.

I turned off the ignition and studied the Atlas to plot a path. Peeled off the cargo pants, took off the long sleeved t-shirt, leaving me in a dago-t that looked natural on a hot L.A. day for a slacker just wandering around. Used the shirt to wipe down every surface inside the Lexus, making a mental note to always make sure to wear gloves in my g-rides until I was back in my own car. I'd removed them to look less conspicuous, but soon realized wiping away fingerprints was too time-consuming.

I started walking, trying to keep my nerves steady, knowing I had about two miles to go to reach my car. As I heard the chopper get close, I ducked into the closest mini-mart. Sweating bullets, I stepped to the cooler and grabbed a couple Miller Lite tall boys, then quickly changed my mind and muttered to myself, "dumb motherfucker." I put the tall boys back and grabbed a Gatorade, thinking I might have to do some running if I was spotted. The cashier was an old Mexican lady, who rang me up and unable to speak English, pointed to the total on the register that was as old as her. I reached into the backpack, trying to hide the contents from her view. I was in such a hurry I handed her a twenty and told her to keep the change as I grabbed the Gatorade and rushed out.

Every time I heard the sound of chopper blades, I ducked into shaded spots beside garages or trees and let it pass. Took me over an hour to go two miles, but once my Charger was in view across the park I broke into a run. I got in, started it, and as soon as I pulled away from the curb I felt a sense of euphoria. Knowing it wouldn't last I dug into a side pocket of the back-pack and grabbed a handful of loose Norcos and chewed them up, washing the pills down with a warm Lite from the glove box.

Hopped on the 170 South. The constant pumping of adrenaline through my body left me exhausted, sweaty and craving a cold shower. As I concentrated on doing the speed limit, I noticed the clock on the stereo read two-thirty. "Fuck," I growled as I pulled out my phone and turned it on. I had five missed calls and three unread text messages, all from Timmy.

I called him back and he answered right away. "Yo Mick, where you at my man? Me and Jackie have been at the office for nearly an hour."

"Hey kid, I got jammed up at this thing out in the Valley" I said, which made my heart race just as fast as if the cops were tailing me again. My conscience punishing me for being an out-of-control, undependable liar. I threw out my own accusation to cover up my guilt. "Wait, it's only two-thirty. Thought Jackie had a test at two, so how did you guys get from Westwood to the office so fast?"

Timmy paused, caught off guard. "Mick, not sure what you're saying but we're here waiting. What's your ETA, buddy?"

I couldn't respond. My mind and words frozen. I looked at myself in the rearview, thinking of how bad I just wanted to hit my loft, swallow more opioids, and take a long shower while chugging cold beers. Timmy said something else, but his words came out as indecipherable sounds like the teacher on Charlie Brown. Shame overcame me as images of my mother flashed before me. Looking in the mirror I didn't see myself. I saw her mouth, her lips, her face. I could hear her conniving voice in my head.

In one violent motion I ripped off the rearview and attempted to throw it out the window that wasn't open. Still attached to wires, it ricocheted and whacked me on the temple, snapping my attention back to reality in time to slam on the brakes. The Brembos screamed and the rubber shrieked and at the last second I steered my skid onto the shoulder, avoiding a rear-end collision with a black SUV bringing up the tail of a traffic jam.

My heartbeat was a rapid, heavy bass drum. My hands clutched the wheel in a sweaty death grip. After a few deep breaths I hit the switch to lower the window, turning to look at the driver of the SUV. He was Latino, short-cropped hair, wrap-around sunglasses. Then I realized the side of his SUV had the "California Highway Patrol" logo emblazoned on it. As I sat there in shock he didn't look at me, just kept looking down at something in his lap as the SUV crept forward in the traffic. How he didn't notice me almost smash into him I will never know. But I took it as a sign that day wasn't the day I'd be destroyed and I needed to fucking get ahold of myself.

I waited for a few cars to pass, then eased back into traffic as I grabbed the phone off the floor that'd flown off my lap. "Sorry Timmy, what'd you say?"

His words were clear now. "Just asking your ETA?"

"I'll be there in forty-five," I said and hung up. I felt warm blood trickle onto my finger from a cut near my temple. I flipped the visor, looked in the vanity mirror, and there was a gash above my right eyebrow. Tried wiping off the blood with a t-shirt as I got off at Laurel Canyon and drove to the top of the mountain. Turned onto Mulholland and drove until I reached a deserted roadside lookout and parked. The fury subsided and in its place was a growing anticipation as I unzipped the backpack and did a rough count of the money. Well over a hundred grand.

CHAPTER 10
CASSAVETTES

pulled into the production office parking lot and backed the Charger up to the door, the trunk full of Miller Lites I'd picked up from the "Rock N' Roll Ralph's" on Sunset. And there was Timmy holding court, the cast and crew huddled around him as he animatedly regaled them with one of his hilarious South Boston stories. Jackie was seated on the hood of Timmy's east coast rusted 94' Nissan Sentra, smoking a cigarette.

Being in their company and knowing the film's financial status was healthy enough to start production, I swelled with pride and stopped obsessing about the point of no return I'd crossed. Soon as Jackie saw me she headed my way, a smile on her face as if the awkward scene the night before never happened. But something was off. Even the sight of her curly golden hair bouncing as she walked towards me didn't have its natural luster. I wished I couldn't see the fracture in her soul, but it was too late.

As I tried wiping off any dried blood from my face, I knocked the backpack onto the floorboard, inches out of my reach as bundles of cash fell out in plain sight. Just as Jackie tried the passenger door I locked it, giving me time to push the backpack and cash beneath the seat.

I unlocked the door and she opened it, "you made it."

"Of course, kid. With beers in the trunk." Was hoping the request to help grab beers would divert her attention from my face, but I couldn't hide the fresh gash over my brow.

"Oh my God, Mickey. What the hell happened?"

"Ah, just some stupid shit," I said as I climbed out and stepped to the trunk.

She reached a tentative hand to the wound. "Jesus," she said softly.

I tried playing it off by grabbing a case of beer with each hand and giving her a kiss on the way to the door. "What's with all the God-Jesus talk, Jack? Were you really studying at Liana's house last night or were you seeing a priest behind my back?"

"He's not a priest yet, he's still in seminary school," she shot back.

"There she is," I said, smiling.

She giggled and opened the door for me, "everybody's so excited you made it." Her eyes got wide as she smiled, flashing her teeth in that sexy way she did without knowing. For a moment her verve was back, and after going through what I'd gone through that day was good enough to help me temporarily push all the stress and fear from my being and once again become the giver of hope.

"Yo Cassavetes! Let's go kid," I yelled over to my director Timmy and his adoring crew. "Grab the beers and hoagies from the trunk and let's do this!

The Sunset Strip address was sexy on paper, but in reality the office definitely was not. The drop-ceiling tiles were stained, sagging or missing. Chipped Formica counters. Oxidized steel desks. An ancient, moldy Rolodex disintegrating atop one of them. A single bathroom with a lopsided, low-flow toilet. It wasn't glamorous, but it did have a big professional-looking sign that read "79th Street" in cool movie font on the door. Giving me a feeling of accomplishment that made it all worthwhile, however fleeting.

Most people never chase their dreams. They weld beams, flip burgers, stock shelves, create spreadsheets. They punch clocks and toe the line, hoping to sustain their safe and boring little worlds. Staring at that sign with the name of a film that I'd written and was about to shoot sent a chill down my spine, knowing it was a bigger chance than most people would ever take in their entire lives.

Just like I could read her soul, Jackie caught me staring and must've caught a glimpse of mine. Her arms slid around me, our bodies fitting like puzzle pieces, her hair smelling like shampoo and cigarettes. We stood there staring at the sign, her heart thumping against my chest almost as hard as mine had pounded all day. Jackie wasn't humoring me but sharing the same creative buzz I was feeling. She leaned back and studied the gash on my head that was still raw and red.

"Mickey…" she said, wanting to know the truth.

Before she dug too deep I cut her off, "whattya say we take a road trip to Vegas this weekend?" It came to me like most things, in the firing of a synapse. An idea that could kill two birds with one stone. Resetting things with Jackie on a romantic weekend out of town, allowing us to come clean with our secrets. And changing the hundred grand from Chase into casino chips to wash any possibly marked bills.

"Maybe," she said, sounding both intrigued and sad. "Come on, let's officially open '79th Street'."

Having overheard, Timmy approached. "That's still a working title, but it's starting to stick with me." He then addressed the cast and crew, "ladies and gents, welcome to the office of Rag Tag Productions. As most of you know, this ruggedly handsome fella here is Mickey. A triple-threat, he's the writer, producer and financier."

"Hey Mick, thanks for the awesome opportunity," said Joe

Saccaro.   The young, about-to-break, male lead Timmy had convinced to sign on for SAG minimum.

"No. Thank you for bein' a part of this. Lookin' good, Joe!" I scanned the dozens of faces, trying to switch from bank robber mode to filmmaker mode as I put names to faces. "I haven't officially met all you guys, but I see Adama. I say that right?"

Adama was our Senegalese cinematographer.   Female, tall, exotic, great eyes and a great eye.   "Yes Mickey, you said it correctly and I'm impressed you remembered."

"How could I forget. Adama Diallo, the name almost sounds Italian. But I was most impressed with your short film about the soccer player turned gunrunner. Dark and raw and heavy, but full of beauty and light," my words elicited a visible blush, even on her skin as dark as espresso. "Well listen guys, we got beers and Hoagies."

"Hoagies," Jackie cut in, smiling at Timmy.

"Who the fuck calls sub sandwiches hoagies?" Timmy grandstanded and exchanged deadpan looks with Jackie.

"Alright, so let's bust the old timer's balls," I said to chuckles around the room.   "Like I was sayin', grab a beer and a sandwich. I can't wait to meet the rest of you, I'm gonna track down some cleaning supplies and we'll get this show on the road when I get back," I said, motioning for Timmy to follow me as I headed for the door.

Grabbed a pack of Parliament Lights from my car and we had a smoke outside. "Hey Mick, I know you told me you're taking care of the money side of things, but if you need a hand convincin' investors I'm down to ride."

"Listen kid, I see how people pay attention when you speak, you're a great storyteller and a natural leader," our eyes met and leveled as I said this. "You're the captain of this ship, so here," I flicked the cigarette and ducked back into the car. I reached under the seat and grabbed the backpack, unzipped it, and handed over a handful of the cash. "Let's go make this fuckin' movie."

Afternoon turned into night and the pre-production meeting turned into a party. Timmy was in rare form, entertaining as always, but I witnessed a transformation. He traded his usual crude street sense anecdotes for a warmer deference in his introductions, finding precision segues to the production moving forward and creating a family vibe. Maybe it was the cash I handed him that put him in a professional state of mind. The Lites were running low around nine so I walked to a 7/11 and picked up another case and a bottle of Hornitos. I had been pounding the beers to stave off feeling the onset of withdrawals and walking down Sunset my footsteps were heavy with drunkenness.

On the way back I thought about Jackie, realizing she said less and less as the party wore on. I stopped at the Charger, saying out loud, "fuck. Did she leave?" Adrenaline shot through me like lightning as I tried the passenger side handle. The door opened and I saw a piece of paper on the seat, but ignored it as I searched under the seat. The cash was still there but my skull was pounding with shame and carelessness. I grabbed the piece of paper from the front seat, unfolded it and was hit with the scent of her skin.

Hey,

Don't take this the wrong way but I'm going to spend some time by Liana's house. You already know I get this way sometimes. I just need some time to think and I know you have a lot to do right now with the movie and whatnot. You're probably thinking, I was just out of town for two weeks and she needs time alone? Fuck, I don't know Mick. I need a change of scenery I guess. I want you to know I'm always thinking of you. So don't go wandering off too far, I may still need you to come find me in the night.

LUV U,

Jackie
p.s. I stole your White Sox pullover XOXO

Had mixed emotions about Jackie's note, but in all honesty I'd been expecting her to cut bait sooner or later. Not feeling particularly sociable just then, I got behind the wheel and took off, leaving Timmy and the celebration behind. I remember driving with one eye shut, trying to see straight as the alcohol and pills and exhaustion hit me all at once. I don't remember driving to Echo Park and passing out in my car. But that's where I woke up early in the morning. I drove back to the loft in a dream state. I didn't feel sad about Jackie. I just drove.

CHAPTER 11
FACCIAMO UN BRINDISI

locked the deadbolt behind me, grabbed two beers from the fridge and dropped the backpack on the coffee table. Cracked open a bottle, stared at the backpack for a few seconds and in a show of restraint I turned on some music and took a four-beer shower.

In the shower my thoughts were wild. Dollars danced through my head for a minute or two, then I thought about how striking the woman from the bank was. I even fantasized about the way she helped me and what it would be like to run into her sometime. A scenario appeared to me; I'm in Vegas, poolside at one of those adults only pools, as women frequently walked around topless. I'd have a cabana with some friends. They would all be standing around talking to girls, I'd be alone on the day bed sipping a vodka tonic. She'd be sitting across the way, on the other side of the shallow pool, tanning by herself wearing a thong and glamorous oversized sunglasses, nothing else. She'd catch me watching her and give me a little wave and a devilish grin. I'd grin back and she'd point an imaginary handgun at me, fire one imaginary shot, and blow the smoke away like a kid might do. Then I thought of Jackie. I snapped out of my fantasy and toweled off.

I was stunned as I sat there on the couch staring at it piled up into three stacks on the coffee table. It wasn't that I'd never seen that much cash before because I had seen more than that when I was a young boy upstairs in my uncle's tavern. It was where he brought his gambling operation's collections and did his books. By the time I was five I was somewhat of a mathematical prodigy. I'd do my uncle's counting from time to time. He'd always give me a c-note for my services. I always gave that money to my father to help with the bills or groceries. Same as back in the day, I was amazed at the ease in which I had just come upon that much money. I jumped up from the couch, got dressed, wrapped the money in tinfoil, stashed it behind frozen pizzas in the freezer and drove to a Staples down Wilshire.

The safe was about eighteen inches cubed, almost the same exact size as the one at the bank earlier that day. It weighed every bit of seventy pounds. Once I put all the cash from the two banks inside it didn't seem like that much. But it was easy for me to imagine this thing full before long. I felt a need to relax somehow, take my mind off of everything. I threw on some shorts, walked to the liquor store a couple blocks down Main, bought a twelve pack and hit the rooftop pool.

No surprise, it looked like spring break. The crowd was mostly young, early to mid-twenties. Beautiful people without a care in the world, or so they portrayed that image with their partying ways while the rest of the people in America were grinding through monotonous daily lives. I walked through the crowd acting aloof, looking for Timmy. I knew at least half of these kids and gave brief and cordial smiles or pats on shoulders each time somebody said hello. I did not feel like stopping to make small talk so I said not even a 'what's up' as I made an entire lap on the pool deck. No Timmy. I walked into the garden area where the grill pits and couches were. I spotted my director holding court surrounded by a group of pretty girls. A young guy I did not know was manning the grill and there were wine and liquor bottles and mixers littering the table nearby.

As I approached, Timmy acknowledged me with a nod, finished his sentence, and segued seamlessly into an introduction. "But let me interrupt this fuckin' bullshit lie of a story to introduce a man that is the real deal." I set the twelve pack on the table, ripped it open and grabbed one for me, handed him one. He twisted the top off and let it drop to the ground and reached his beer to me. We toasted as he was already speaking again, "Fuckin' Mickey Fortunato," as if he hadn't seen me in years, with each arm around a girl, "Mick, I'd like you to meet Melissa," he nodded his head to the girl on his far right and proceeded clockwise. "Jeanette, Erica, Emily, and, uh…," to the girl closest to me, "what was your name again sweetheart? Wait! Don't tell me…" She was giggling in a supremely SoCal way. "Lilly." He said matter-of-factly.

"Leonora!" The other girls said in an uproar followed with inebriated laughter. It was obvious at this point that Timmy was showing them a good time and the vibe was exactly what I was looking for. "Hi Mickeyyyy," they chorused again in perfect harmony.

"Hello ladies," I said acknowledging each one with a smile and a nod. "Any of you girls want a beer? Leonora with the beautiful name, you want a beer?" As was always my way when I met a group of people, I felt a need to include the forgotten, though she was the prettiest one of the lot.

With a gracious smile that lit up her olive skinned face she said, "No thanks. I'm sticking with vino until the sun sets."

"I'll take one," said one of the other ones whose name I'd already forgotten. I handed her one, twisting the top off for her. She had a more than flirtatious smile, sunglasses hiding her eyes and bleach blonde hair pulled back into a ponytail. "Thank you Mickey," and a shake of her head that whipped her hair to one side as she wanted to let me know she liked what she saw.

I obliged her with a warm cool smile, "You're welcome to as many as you want. We run out we'll send Rodney Dangerfield over here," pointing my beer at Timmy who was whispering into

one of the girls' ears, "to the liquor store." As I said this I felt
Lenora's gaze out of the corner of my eye. I turned my attention
to her. "And what will you switch your beverage of choice to
once the day turns to night young Leonora? Will it be as sophis-
ticated as the fine cabernet sauvignon you sip pre-twilight?"

"Wow. You are smooth aren't you, Mickey." She said this
with an ear-to-ear smile. "It remains to be seen if I will still be
here when the sun sets." Leonora said this as she turned
halfway and swept her wraparound covering the bottom half of
her two-piece bathing suit to sit down at the end of the couch.
Her demeanor was not the same as the other girls. She had a
sense of grace without being pretentious. I sat in the chair
facing her.

"I wouldn't say 'smooth'. Congenial is a better word in this
instance. I guess I'll just have to wait to find out what you prefer
to imbibe come sundown."

"O.K. you are congenial Mickey. So how do you know
Timmy?"

"I live in the building," I was interrupted by the aforementioned as he took a seat next to Leonora on the couch.

Saying to her with all seriousness, "Leonora, this guy here is
gonna be famous. He's got a story or two to tell that are gonna
turn this town on its head and I'm the man behind the man.
Ain't that right Mick?"

Sliding her shades up into her hair and turning to me, "Oh,
so you're the one that's making a movie. Timmy was telling us
about it. So, what's the story line?"

Timmy's phone began vibrating in his pocket, he pulled it out
to check the number, looked at me then said, "I gotta take this
one my man. Hold down the party, would ya?" He walked
away into the sea of partygoers talking into his phone.

"Where are you from Leonora?"

"If you were to guess, where would you think I was from?"

"I'd say right here in L.A. Born and raised in.." I scanned her
once, head to toe, noticing a tattoo of musical notes starting on

her right ankle and winding down to the top of her foot. " the Valley….No..wait..Venice, by the beach," I said with confidence.

"Very good, wow. May I ask how you came to this conclusion? Have we met before?" She said this, paused and took a sip of wine as she re-crossed her legs.

"Your accent, or lack thereof tells me you are not from any place east of the Mississippi. It's SoCal to be sure. I was almost thrown into jumping to stereotypes when I began to say the Valley, what with that long, straight, lustrous mane of black hair you have. Then I noticed the tattoo," pointing my beer toward her ankle, "It seemed quite bohemian in nature, very Venice." I shot her an impish smile.

"Very fuckin' smooth'" she said and began laughing, almost being coy. "So are you going to tell me about this movie you're making?"

"Have you ever seen 'Goodfellas'?"

"Martin fuckin' Scorcese. Of course I know 'Goodfellas'."

"Well, this movie is nothing like that," I dead-eyed.

She looked at me, eyes squinting, "OK, so you don't want to talk about the movie. Where are you from? Wait, let me guess." Our rapport was evident. This was fun I had to admit. "I would have to say on accent alone that you are from somewhere on the east coast, maybe Boston…Philly?"

I stonewalled her, remaining silent with a grin on my face.

She continued with, "but you seem a bit too humble without being passive so I'm gonna have to say you are from Chicago, yeah definitely Chicago but the accent is quite particular. You're Italian." We stared at each other for about three seconds and both started laughing. She was smiling brilliantly now. If she had a guard, it was dropped. "The Bohemian in me wants to ask a question about your past."

"The past has passed. In the moment seems an appropriate tense to me. You live in the moment Leonora?" As these words left my lips I felt a rush of guilt for losing myself in this flirtatious give and take. I pounded the rest of my now half warm beer and reached for her empty glass. I stood, grabbed another beer and refilled her wine. As I sat back in the chair she was already holding her glass toward me.

"Facciamo un brindisi," she said, her sunglasses back over her eyes now.

"OK, so the girl from Venice Beach knows some Italian," I said stifling a chuckle. "What should we toast to?"

"To the moment."

"And may we always live in it," I added. "Chin." We clinked glasses, tapped the bottoms on the table, and drank. Jackie was in the back of my mind, this intriguing Leonora in the fore, the previous few days nowhere to be found. I was behind the wheel but the road was driving.

"What do you wanna do tonight, kid?" I said loud enough to be heard over the desert's night air blowing through the SRT8. We sped up Interstate 15 at a hundred and twenty miles an hour.

"Whatever man, I can't even believe we're going to Vegas right now. I mean, this is fuckin' crazy," she said fighting to keep her hair pinned behind her ears. "See where the night takes us, right?" she stole a look at me.

For the first time in about an hour I turned to look at her. Her big brown eyes were smiling and filled with life and adventure. I was melancholy and lustful all the same. Our eyes met as if we were in love and I smiled and said, "What's your favorite thing to do in Vegas?"

"I was only there once, for a friend's twenty first birthday. Ten girls, two shitty rooms at Circus Circus. It was a hot mess. Fun though, from what I can remember of it," Leonora said.

"I never asked how old you were." As I said this I looked over and gave her a closer look. She was older than Jackie for sure, by a year or two? Maybe I'd thought she hadn't even experienced Las Vegas yet.

"Twenty seven. Why? How old did you think I was?" The tone in her voice was playful but self-conscious about being north of twenty-five, that being an age when most of the girls in LA start to feel that imaginary clock ticking.

"I hadn't thought about it to tell you the truth. I'm older, you're younger, what difference does it make?" Widening her eyes and giving me a punch to the shoulder, "That says a lot. So you like em' young, huh Mickey? How come a guy like you doesn't have a girl?"

She caught me off guard with the question. I let it hang for a few seconds, processed and decided not to answer.

"You DO have a girlfriend. Wow. You didn't say anything about her all day on the rooftop," her voice not the least bit offended by this realization. "Where does she think you are? You tell her you were driving to Vegas with a girl just you met at the pool today?"

"You never asked if I had a lady," I said this feeling my alter ego taking full control. "Anyway, my girl said she needed a change of scenery, time to think. Along those lines. What about you? You got a man, Leonora?"

"No chance. Not a lot of men out there. Plenty of boys though, that's Los Angeles for ya. Doesn't really matter cuz I'm not looking for anything serious at the moment," she said staring ahead, the smile gone from her face, her hands clasped in her lap. "How long ago did she leave?"

I lucked out as we came up on an exit for a gas station. I hit the off ramp and redirected the conversation, "We're about an hour out, figured it'd be a good time to hit the men's room. Sure you'd like to check yourself out before we walk into a hotel lobby on a hot Vegas night. I gotta gas this thing up anyway, runnin' low kid." We were already stopped at the pump, I killed the engine and jumped out before she could say anything. I closed the door and walked around to the passenger side, her door still closed. I opened it and offered my hand to help her out. She was staring at me, cheeks slightly flushing as her smile reappeared. She took my hand like she was in an evening gown and heels and I was helping her out of a limo to the red carpet. We continued this charade to the door at the storefront which I opened displaying perfect manners. Her hair in a ponytail now, she said nothing as she continued to the restrooms. She looked incredible. I grabbed a cold six-pack of Miller Lite tall boys, prepaid the gas and hurried to the car.

I popped the trunk, set the six-pack inside and zipped open my backpack. I pulled out a handful of pills and popped em', chewing them into bits, cracked a cold one and drowned what was left of my conscience, pounding all twenty-four ounces. Grabbed the remaining five by the empty plastic ring, closed the trunk and started the pump.

It was peaceful staring out into the desert night but I knew the tranquility was a mirage. I popped another beer, took a huge pull and immediately felt the expanse of my day. I had about a hundred thousand in cash and three hundred painkillers in a backpack in the trunk. I'm an hour outside of Las Vegas with a girl that I don't know anything about but I could easily fall for. The girl I was sure I was in love with had left me the day before and for all I really knew, the FBI could already be hunting for me. I thought maybe I'll just see where the road takes me. I wasn't sure if I trusted my own judgment at this point anyway.

"Hey," I heard her voice from a distance. "You gonna use the little boys room?"

I turned and Leonora was coming toward me, tearing the cellophane off a pack of Parliament Lights. The gas stopped pumping, I handed her a beer. Her eyes went wide when she grabbed the over-sized beer can, giving me an incredulous look that said "Fuck it." Her glistening full lips said, "I guess this answers the question of the day."

"Ceremonious it may be, but I always drink a few beers on the homestretch to the Strip," I said, then clanked cans with her. She chugged half the can as I finished mine, handed her the empty then walked inside to the men's room.

I had to piss but the pills made it difficult. I turned on the faucet, let the water run, entered a stall and closed the door. I stood there for a good two minutes before a stream started. By then my mind was going off the rails. And though I was playing the role of cool guy with the girl in my car, I was hearing dueling voices in my head telling me things like "turn the fuckin' car around and get rid of this chick," or "you've come this far, you might as well have some fun, you may never even see Jackie again anyways." I finished, zipped up and went and splashed cold water over my face. I exited the men's room and made my way out the door.

"Man, that's some sweet ride you got there fella," said the clerk. He was a tall man probably in his mid to late sixties with a build that said he'd probably been a force to be reckoned with in his prime. "Girl ain't bad either," he stated matter-of-factly.

I stopped at his counter only because he'd said something. "Yeah man, she's alright I guess," I said staring out the window at Leonora siting in the passenger seat, smoking a cigarette. "Marlboro Reds."

He grabbed the cigarettes and placed them on the counter. I noticed some old faded jailhouse tats on his left forearm and knuckles. The one on his knuckles read 'OVER', one letter on each finger. I couldn't see it because he was punching the register with it but I guessed his right hand read 'GAME'. I'd seen this tattoo once before. It was on the hand of an old timer in my uncle's tavern when I was a kid. Rocky Ruffalo was his name but guys simply called him Rock. He was one of the last prisoners in Alcatraz when its doors were boarded up back in the sixties. The first time I'd seen his knuckle tattoo it reminded me of those words on the Space Invaders game. Rock was probably long dead by now, but this clerk bore a striking resemblance. "My uncle had that same tat on his hand," I lied but I felt an urge to talk to this guy for a minute.

He held up both fists hovering over the counter to prove me right. "You do a long stretch and somewhere along the line you realize that everything comes to an end. I know that seems pretty heavy to a young buck like you but it's the truth." He said this with a warm smile. I think he was actually pretty happy to be a cashier in the twilight of his days.

I stared at him for a few seconds. "I'm a long way from home right now. Everything seems heavy these days," I said returning a smile of humility. I pulled a twenty from my roll and handed it to him.

He gave me my change and said, "I know you and your girlfriend out there are probably burnin' up the pavement on your way to Sin City but it ain't goin' anywhere. Take yer time and enjoy the ride man, in your prime."

I nodded back and said over my shoulder as I turned to walk out, "I'll catch you on the flip side, Rock."

When I got back in the car Leonora handed me another tallboy as we were returning to the highway. She was sipping one and not saying anything. I think she sensed that my mind was elsewhere.

I kept the speedometer at a hundred all the way into Vegas. The atmosphere inside the car had changed from whimsy to reality once the lights of the city appeared. The pills and the booze had me in a mood of indestructibility as soon as I saw and felt the energy of this desert city of debauchery and dreams.

I valeted at the Venetian and neither of us said a thing about the irony and we walked in as if we owned the joint.

"Why don't you go grab us a couple drinks while I get a room," I said this, handed her a fifty and grabbed her bag from her. As she began to walk away, "I'll make sure there's two beds, unless you want a separate room?"

She stopped and turned to face me from twenty feet away, smiling, "Call your sweetie."

"Hey, don't go too far, there's a bar right around that corner, easy to get lost in this place, trust me," I said, pointing with my finger.

I brought our bags over to the counter and slid my players

card, I.D., and a credit card wrapped in a c-note to the hostess. I told her I was looking for an upgraded suite. She looked up my player rating and was more than happy to oblige. She told me I was in luck and that they had a two bedroom, three bathroom, full bar with living room and two hot tub suite. She also told me that I'd get the player's rate of a hundred dollars a night. I told her I'd take it for three nights, grabbed the keys and walked toward the bar. Leonora was just leaving with two mixed drinks in her hands when I reached her. I set the bags down, grabbed one of the glasses, took a sip and handed it back to her. "Vodka Red Bull. Good call kid…if you don't wanna remember anything in two days."

"I figured we'd need a little boost before we conquer the night. You checked in already?" she asked, I nodded as I scanned the surroundings. "That was fast." She drank the entire drink and left the glass on the ashtray.

Upon entering the suite I was transformed into a different person. It was palatial with high ceilings and a bar with a pool table. V.I.P. I acted casual, as if I'd stayed in this suite a hundred times and walked straight to the second bedroom.

Leonora came out of the master bedroom, "What the fuck! Oh my god, I've never even seen anything like this," she was looking around in awe as she approached the bar.

I set her bag on the sofa at the edge of the bed. I walked to the bar and surveyed the drinking options with my backpack still on my shoulder, duffel bag in hand.

She looked at me, no smile, her eyes a mile wide, trying to be cool, "so this is how you roll? Wow, pretty fuckin' groovy, I gotta say."

I reached down and opened the mini fridge and grabbed two Miller Lites, popped the tops and gave her one. "My golden rule in Vegas, stick to beer. You can keep a steady buzz if you drink light beer, keep the party goin', any hangover you might get can easily be slayed with breakfast room service."

She stared, smiling as she took a long drink. "So Mick, what's next? What are we getting into? I didn't bring clothes for the clubs."

Staring out the window, we had an unobstructed view of the strip. Rising up to about three or four stories below us was a new wing adjoining the Venetian, called the Palazzo. The construction site at midnight was lighted and there were men working. Welding sparks fell as ironworkers worked for straight overtime, beating the heat as they say, night work. After a few seconds of flashing back to that type of work, I said over my shoulder, "Let's stroll through the casino, see if any table appears inviting. You play blackjack?"

"That's where you get twenty-one, right?"

"Yeah, that's the one, "Who knows, maybe we'll make a few bucks and go shopping tomorrow, buy some threads to hit a club or two at night."

She finished the beer and threw the empty in the trash behind the bar, patted me on the ass and walked past saying, "I'm going to freshen up a little."

"I'll be here kid," I said.

Looking out into the neon sky I was thinking how natural it felt to be around her. Then it dawned on me. After what I'd done in the last few days I wanted companionship and didn't want to feel the burden of my secret life, my lies. Deep down I knew that I should try to see Jackie and ease her mind if that's what she wanted. But the path of least resistance appealed to me at this point. I was fast learning to justify every one of my actions. Selfish as I felt, it eased my conscience.

I grabbed another two beers and went to the safe where I stashed my cash and pills, grabbed five grand in hundreds and added it to my roll. I changed into the black designer jeans from my bag and threw on a polo, checked myself in the mirror. I was tan going on burnt, my eyes looked weary, but overall I looked surprisingly good. I touched up my hair with a little pomade. It was short and messy, faded on the sides. Brushed my teeth and rinsed with Miller Lite. I went back to the bar to do a shot of

Don Julio and watch the ironworkers weld into the Las Vegas night until Leonora was ready.

The shot went down with a smoothness and the warmth from the tequila soothed my nerves. Chased it with a beer and was pouring another shot when Leonora appeared from her room. She looked as if she had been getting ready for hours. She was wearing dark blue jeans, a white spaghetti strap cotton halter that accentuated her taught body. Her hair was down and had soft hints of curls now, topped off with a hounds tooth flat cap. The only make-up visible was eyeliner and lip-gloss high-lighting her natural features that were sensual if not flawless. As she walked toward me at the bar I noticed the silver hoops in her ears. Her effortless look made me forget the mayhem that wracked my conscience. "Are you gonna pour me one of those shots?" She surprised me when she drew close and kissed me on the lips. We were inhabiting roles in a fantasy, playing off of one another. I poured her a shot. "Facciamo un Brindisi," she said for the second time in eight hours.

"To a beautiful day. And to you, Leonora from Venice, for being so breezy on this jaunt. May the gods of fortune shine on you." I said, feeling my mojo meeting my loquaciousness halfway sober.

She stood close, staring into my eyes as if she knew more than she did and said, "If you write half as good as you talk then Timmy was right, you will be famous. To the gods of fortune." She shot the tequila like a pro.

"I'll give it to ya Leonora, you're a pretty cool chick, you got balls and a sense of adventure."

"There's something different about you Mick."

"Oh yeah, besides my accent?"

"I don't know. You're sure of yourself. But your eyes look like they're always trying to figure out a better way. That doesn't even make sense, does it," she said with her cheeks showing color, eyes staring me down. This girl was speaking to my soul. And like everything about her, it seemed effortless. I had met Jackie's spiritual doppelgänger.

"Look kid, I wasn't trying to steer this conversation into the deep end. We're in Vegas," I said, pouring more Don Julio.

We downed the shots without a toast and she said, "So how much does a room like this run, for a night?"

"I don't even know. Most people that stay in rooms like this don't know either. Suites like this are usually comped. The casino is throwing something at you under the guise that you're getting something for nothing."

"I see."

"But as the saying goes, ain't nothing free in the fuckin' world," I said and turned toward the window.

"So you show up and they gave you this ridiculous room gratis because they know you will lose a lot of money whenever you're here. What happens if you win?"

"We'll just have to see now, won't we." I deadpanned for a moment as she started to giggle. "Whenever you gamble you get rated. They keep track of how much you wager and how long you play. The more you wager and longer you gamble the more 'free' stuff they give you."

"They keep track of you all the time?"

"Casinos track everyone, security cameras and whatnot, but to get rated they average out your wagers. I sit down, hand over my card, and the pit boss tracks my bets."

She processed this new information. "How much did you lose last time you were here? You know, for them to give you a room like this?"

"How about let's go see if a table looks good, whattya say?"

CHAPTER 12

THOUSAND IN GREEN, THOUSAND IN BLACK

"So what are we looking for, how do you know if a table will be lucky?" she said as we strolled, hand in hand, on the floor of the casino that was abuzz with tourists, beautiful people, degenerates, gamblers.

"The first thing I look for is a table that does not have a continuous shuffle, which is becoming more popular. That means every time a hand is finished, the cards are swept up by the dealer and put into a little machine that adds them to the shuffle. The house eliminates any skill or strategy a smart player might have, like card counters. That's why I like casinos like this one, no continuous shuffle yet." I said. We stopped to watch the play at a table. There were four players and third base, the last spot to be dealt on the table, was open.

"Isn't counting cards illegal?"

Leaning close to her, "I'm not exactly counting cards per se, I'm simply watching the flow of the cards using simple math skills. This table's lookin good so far. Let's watch how the cards come out for a minute." I slid into the empty seat at third base as she stood next to me. The minimum wager on this table was standard, twenty-five dollars with a maximum bet of ten thousand. That night I wanted to play leisurely, but win.

The four players at the table were obviously traveling together, three of them dressed like they just robbed a St. Louis Cardinals souvenir stand. Two couples, probably in their late thirties, all playing the table minimum and enjoying drinks on the house. I could tell that the cards were running good as three of the players had hundreds of dollars in chips in front of them. The second I sat down, the lady with the short stack hit four blackjacks in a row. The cards were running hot.

"You guys want me to wait for the next shoe," I said to the other players as a common courtesy.

"Come on in while the getting's good brother," said one of the men in a rural southern accent.

I reached in my pocket, pulled my roll out, kept it below the table, slid out my player's card out and grabbed a wad of hundreds. I placed two thousand on the table. The dealer counted out the cash on the table and a cocktail waitress appeared.

"Two Miller Lites," Leonora said as I watched the dealer finish the count. I grinned at her.

The dealer was a docile and polite young woman, late twenties with a Mediterranean complexion. Her nametag read Federica. Her hands moved deftly with steady graceful motions, all one speed. "Two thousand on a player's card," she said over her shoulder to the pit boss. "How would you like that Mr. Fortunato?" she said.

The pit boss, a dignified looking man in his forties, salt and pepper hair, tailored suit, grabbed my players card from her hand.

"Thousand in green, thousand in black will be fine. Thank you Federica," I said rolling the 'r' in her name, making her smile.

"Always mister smooth," Leonora whispered into my ear. Her breath was warm with tequila.

"Alright man, I like this guy's style, commin' in swinging," said one of the guys sitting at the table who had obviously been enjoying the free drinks.

I looked at him with a casual grin and noticed his t-shirt. St. Louis Cardinals World Series Champs 2006. The dealer stacked my chips, slid them to me, and immediately I felt good about the universe.

"Are you staying with us Mr. Fortunato," asked the pit boss.

"Yes sir."

I counted cards in blackjack. Using advanced basic strategy, I paid attention to the flow of the cards and adjusted my bet accordingly. The more low cards dealt in the last several hands I raised my bet. Lowered it after a run of mostly high cards. When the cards were running a steady mix of low and high I played according to my chip stack, conservative and cagey. I almost always played with discipline, knowing when to press a bet, but more importantly, knowing when to get up and walk away. This was the trick to winning more than you lose.

Thinking that I'd give her the crib notes later on my skills, I slid all ten black chips out for my first wager. The move was not my style but the impulse hit from the same part of the brain making my decisions these days. A thousand dollars wagered on the first hand. Was sure that the presence of Leonora played a part in this leap. "Check's played," the dealer said over her shoulder.

Speaking in a hushed tone near my ear Leonora said, "Are you going to explain to me what you're doing. You know, like strategy, so I can play."

My first card was an ace. I held off on my response wanting to see my next card. Five seconds later, a king. Blackjack on my first hand.

"Fucking A, man!" said the Cardinals fan. The rest of the table reacted with excitement.

I remained stoic. The dealer flipped her show card. A six. I made fifteen hundred on the first hand. My head half turned to Leonora I said, "that's my strategy in a nutshell," then I turned to look her in the eye. "Get lucky." We both started laughing. I looked back at the table, my winnings still sitting next to my original wager, cards already swept, the tourists stayed with 19's and 20's.

"Come on, bust!" said the woman sitting at first base. The dealer flipped her hole card, it was a nine. She drew a queen and busted. The table went wild as the two couples combined to win a hundred dollars. Impulse dictating my every move, I pressed my bet, twenty five hundred out there now. My heart raced, but only for a moment.

The cocktail waitress showed up with our beers as the next hand was being dealt. I handed the waitress a green chip. She was an aging beauty, buxom with long curly brown hair, late thirties and smoker's lines at the edges of her mouth and eyes. "Very sweet of you honey," she said in regards to my tip.

Shot her a smile and turned to see the dealer laying an ace on top of my first card, a ten. The table erupted in applause, I held my breath to see the dealer's show card. It was a king. Leonora, not knowing what's going on but rather reacting to the other players, was hugging me. It was in haste. I never celebrated but rather portrayed an attitude of indifference at the table regardless of the action. The same way I'd react in my youth playing sports. Score a touchdown, hit a home run. Let your teammates act a fool. The old man taught me to act like you'd been here before and you'll be here again. It was business as usual.

The dealer slid the cards over to the electronic scanner, tucked the corner into the slot to check if the bottom card was an ace. If the card was an ace I'd push, not lose my wager. The dealer did not have an ace. I felt a wave of euphoria wash over me but contained myself. Forgotten was the fact that I had robbed two banks in the last few days. Forgotten was the fact that Jackie had left me to think about things. It wasn't even a thought that if I kept pressing my luck I'd end up losing my stack in the next two minutes should fate reach out and teach me a lesson. In the last five minutes I had won over five thousand dollars. A thought flashed through my mind. A big run, a real hot streak on this table could change my life forever and bring an abrupt halt to my career in crime. To do this I'd have to lay it on the line and gamble more than I usually did. I was in outlaw mode. Hubris dominating my actions.

In that moment I decided to go for broke, let the chips fall where they may. I pressed the next bet. Blackjack again. There was already a small crowd gathering around the table as the two couples from St. Louis and Leonora raised a raucous cheer. I was now up fifteen grand. It was more than I'd gotten from the first bank. Leonora grabbed my head with both hands and laid a long wet kiss on my cheek. We were all feeling it, everyone at the table, including Federica.

'Be cool' I heard my father's voice in my head.

We stayed at that table for two hours. I paid attention to the cards' flow but not with the usual precision. I rode the wave of excitement, at times playing to the crowd with my bets, but never asking to exceed the table limit from the pit boss. Luck was on my side that night. As the drinks flowed I became surprisingly pragmatic in my decisions. It was easy to do playing with house money from the onset. Somewhere along the way I'd decided I had everything to gain and nothing to lose. Maybe it was in the back of my mind that I had almost a hundred grand in the safe upstairs.

I won more than five hundred grand in those couple of hours. The opiates and alcohol in my bloodstream combined with the excitement and money to overwhelm my senses. I felt the need to gather myself. The fact that I had this presence of mind took me by surprise when I considered my circumstances.

Players always remember the big hits. Playing blackjack upstairs at my uncle's bar as a kid and in casinos starting in my teens, I had won big several times. My biggest hit before was forty grand. It happened at a bachelor party at the Mirage five years ago. It was a legendary tale among the guys back then. Half a million is another realm. Life changing money.

"Well folks, I'm gonna take a break," I said casually but loud enough for the two couples from Missouri to hear me. I pushed all of my chips toward Federica who had just returned to the table from a break. "I was waiting for you to color up."

"Very nice playing sir," she said wearing a professional smile. There were two pit bosses next to her now, each of them rapt in their attention to the count. One looming over each of her shoulders. They looked like twin goons, bookends for a crime boss.

"You done, Big Time?" one of my new friends from the Show Me State said with admiration.

"I'm done for now, my man. It's been a real pleasure meeting you guys," I said giving each of them a nod. They were your typical recreational players, rarely wagering more than the table minimum, soaking up as many house drinks as they could. I was lucky, they all played blackjack according to the book, asking me what they should do in instances they did not know. They respected the fact that I had a lot more at stake on any single hand than they'd wager in their whole trip.

I was watching Federica finish counting the chips and I realized that I had just brought a lot of attention to myself. And as soon as I'd announced I was coloring up, several distinguished looking men of casino staff had appeared from nowhere. Had they been waiting for my declaration of cessation? There was a certain casino protocol to be followed when winnings were of this amount, especially where the player did not have a house credit account.

A tall imposing man, late thirties, bald, Rolex, tailored suit, with a square jaw, appeared next to Leonora. "Congratulations on your winnings Mr. Fortunato, how are you feeling right about now?" he said with a perfect balance of phony friendship and business in his tone. No nametag meant he did not work the main floor of the casino.

"I'm alright I guess, maybe a little tired," I said to the host as he extended his hand to me. We shook.

"Ed Donahue, I'm an executive host. I see that you're already staying in a suite, and who is this pretty woman," already shaking hands with Leonora, "your name miss?"

Blushing but composed, she replied, "Leonora, we're just friends." Elegant and jovial, she played the part to the hilt.

"Five hundred twenty seven thousand, seven hundred," Federica said. I heard her but kept my attention on Ed. The crowd exalted a combination of gasps and applause. Leonora was hypnotic as she stared at the chips, trying to process the amount she had just heard.

"It's a pleasure to meet you both," Ed said as he handed business cards to each of us. "Mr. Fortunato, we can have your chips transported to the cage for you if you'd like to accompany me to my office. We can go over the specific services available to winners of your ilk, sir. We want to make you feel at home. Come on, I'll have some drinks sent to my office, what'll the two of you have?"

"Ed, I appreciate the hospitality, but I just want to stretch out for awhile, maybe come back downstairs later, give you guys a chance to win some of this money back," I said and gave him a wink. It had been years since I had won big money playing blackjack and casinos did not issue tax forms on table game winnings back then. I wasn't about to ask if that'd changed.

"Of course sir. We can hold onto your winnings as a safety precaution. Accessible at your discretion of course, whenever you decide to play," Ed began.

"If it's all the same Ed I'll take the chips with me, I'm superstitious that way."

"Whatever you prefer Mr. Fortunato. You are on status with us here. Simply meaning we at the Venetian are at your disposal, V.I.P. all the way. You have my card so call me for anything, anytime. I'll have these gentlemen escort you to the elevator," Ed said and turned to a pair of security guards, suited and booted with earpieces to complete the secret service look.

I laughed as I noticed Federica had already racked five

hundred thousand dollars and change into a single tray and slid it toward me. "That won't be necessary Mr. Ed, I'll manage. Federica, you've been lovely." I tipped her seventy seven hundred dollars

She smiled and said, "Very generous sir. It was a lot of fun."

I gave another twenty grand to the stunned Cards fans, grabbed the other half million dollars, took Leonora's hand and walked away from the table. I was paranoid. Leonora was speechless. Every patron we passed on the way to the elevator seemed to be whispering and looking at me. We reached the edge of the casino floor and Leonora spoke for the first time in a while.

"I can't believe it, oh my god. So now what? Don't you have to change these chips back to real money?"

CHAPTER 13
ROCK STARS DIE YOUNG

t was four in the morning when we walked into the suite. She poured a couple of shots and I went into my room. As I was punching the keypad to open the safe I felt the warm viscosity of blood on my hand. I straightened up and almost lost my balance, dropped the rack of chips on the bed and hurried to the bathroom to thwart the flow of blood from my nose. I grabbed a towel, leaned my head back, squeezed with one hand and fumbled for the faucet with the other. I caught a glimpse of this mess in the mirror. The sight was alarming, gruesome, humbling. I kept the hold on my nose and wiped the blood from my neck and chin with the other end of the hand towel. It was a heavy flow and it abated. But I knew it would happen again. I cleaned up but did not have to change my shirt. Staring at my reflection the guilt outweighed the elation I should've been wrapped in.

"Hey," her voice came from another room. "Are you OK?"

I did a quick once-over, killed the light and emerged from the bathroom to see her standing in the doorway to the room. There I saw the mess already made. A trail of blood drops on the cream colored carpet from the safe to the bathroom, five thousand dollar chips littering the bed-top. I played it off. "The dry desert air, it always does it to me," I said. "Just a bloody nose, no big deal."

"Are you sure? It looks like a lot of blood," she said as she grabbed my chin with one hand, other hand flat on my chest. "Come here," and led me back to the bathroom. She was gentle and sweet as I followed her lead.

She turned the water on warm, grabbed a washcloth, dipped the corner under the stream and dabbed it at the edge of my nostrils. Her tenderness took over my thoughts and before either of us knew what was happening we were on the bed writhing out of our clothes and exploring every inch of each other's bare skin. The half million dollars in chips crashed to the floor. There was nothing romantic or sensual about it. We were feral. I scooped her from the bed, pinned her against the window and fucked her with the city below. It was over in five minutes of sweat and ecstasy. Her face was flushed, eyes dazed, her hair stuck to her forehead and neck.

I felt the wave of darkness washing over my soul as we laid side by side.

She turned her head and said, "I have a surprise for us."

I watched her walk fully naked for the first time. The soft light of the room amplified my feelings of guilt and shame. She came back in a matter of seconds with a joint between her lips and a lighter in her hand. She plopped down next to me without any self-consciousness. "I feel as if I'm walking uninvited through someone else's dream," she said. "Like this isn't real. I mean, did today actually happen?" She was a world-class beauty but that could not help me out of this disparate state. She lit the joint and took a pull, held it in, rolled on top to straddle me and gave me a shotgun of the fruity smoke. It proved a momentary salve to my depression.

The weed lulled me into a daze with one hit. "Relax kid, when it hits home... this day will be a vivid and exciting memory...if the weed and tequila doesn't erase it by morning."

She laughed and I felt it as her body pressed against me. "Where do we go from here Mickey?"

"Finish this joint and you go to sleep. I'll go for a walk."

Her eyes went back and forth between mine, her smile fixated on my squinted and half stoned eyes, "You're a fuckin' rock star, do you know that?"

"Rock stars die young or fade away. I aspire to neither."

I downed a handful of pills with a Lite when I entered the elevator outside the suite. The smell of Leonora was on my face. She had not showered since I met her. The scent of sweet musk hit a primal nerve. Jackie's voice echoed my old man's mantra in my mind and I saw Leonora speaking them, 'be cool kid'. With fifty grand in my pocket, the voice became inspirational when the handful of painkillers began to dissolve and shake hands with the alcohol in my bloodstream. It was easy, I could justify anything at that moment. Even if this money was snatched back up by the house. I still had more than five hundred grand in the safe upstairs. The guilt and darkness faded to oblivion when the elevator came to a halt. I needed to be alone.

The high limit parlor at dawn was the perfect spot. The world disappeared behind me upon entry. Empty tables except for one where an Asian man sat with his hand on his forehead, cigarette with ash an inch long, hanging from his mouth. My eyes scanned the dealers at the other tables. And there she was. Federica. The purveyor of my fortune earlier that night.

I sat third base at her table. Six decks of cards were splayed out in a rainbow shape. I placed the ten five-thousand dollar chips on the table and she continued as if she had never seen me before. She was a pro. I respected her indifference. "Wasn't expecting to see you in here," I said with a warm smile.

She smiled back, swept up the cards and began her graceful shuffling.

"I thought the casino would've given you a leave of absence after the cards you flipped earlier. But it looks like you got fast tracked to high limit." Minimum bet five hundred dollars. Max bet, fifty grand. I put all ten chips in the wager circle. The pit boss came over and stood next to Federica. He was a stately looking man in his fifties. He reminded me of an English butler.

"Checks played," Federica stated.

"Welcome back Mr. Fortunato," the pit boss said.

Scenarios ran through my mind. Had they been following me on the cameras? Had they stacked the deck and had the same dealer that dealt my winning streak waiting for me to come back down? Why was I sitting back at a blackjack table? I had enough money to shoot the movie and then some. A bad feeling settled into my gut when Federica finished the shuffle and flipped the yellow cut card to me. I thought maybe I'll play one chip at a time. After all, isn't that why I came down here? Sip on a few beers and think about my life?

It was too late. She was dealing the cards and the world around me grew silent, I could see myself sitting there from someone else's vantage point. The first card was a five. Three seconds later my second card came. A six. Federica flipped her show card. A six. "You'll have to excuse me for a few minutes Federica, I only brought these chips with me and I'd like to double down," and as these words came from my mouth the out of body experience became more surreal.

"Not a problem Mr. Fortunato," the pit boss said. "However, sir if you'd like us to provide you with a marker it can be arranged."

"I'll be back in five minutes," I said. My nerves instantly frayed at the thought of taking a marker, losing this hand and then losing all my money back to them in minutes. I tried my best to push the negative thoughts from the fore of my conscience. I could not do it. Even the thought that I had a chance of winning another hundred grand in a single hand did nothing to ease my uneasiness.

Walking to the elevator the casino I came upon a cocktail waitress. She was over the hill with her looks wearing too much makeup of the wrong color to do her face any favors. Her tray was empty but for a half-full bottle of water. I grabbed it from her tray without saying anything and kept walking. I got in the elevator, chewed a Xanax from my pocket and washed it down with the remnants of someone else's water. I was at the twenty seventh floor before the last of the pulverized tablet went down my gullet. I had easily taken sixty pills in the last twenty-four hours. Though this last one hadn't hit me yet, the medicinal flavor was a reminder that I was in perilous territory. My tolerance was herculean in respect to the hydrocodone, but the impossible amount of acetaminophen was making my blood pressure sky high. My heart started to feel as if would leap from my chest and explode. Each pill contained more than three hundred milligrams of acetaminophen. My liver was working overtime to break down the pills and the booze. I was a ticking time bomb and I knew it.

In the suite and made my way down the hall. The door to my room was open and the lights still on. The bed was disheveled. The empty tray, that only fifteen minutes ago had contained enough money to make my dreams come true, was empty on top of the dresser above the door that hid the safe. Did I put the rest in the safe? Was Leonora sleeping in her room? I rushed to the safe, hands shaking, and punched in my code, 2727. Then I remembered, as I stared at my baggie of pills and the cash from the banks. I had gone into the safe to grab more drugs and left the tray of chips on top of the dresser while Leonora prepared to get into the jacuzzi.

I ran to the bathroom. Only water in the tub, and continued with a murderous gait down the hallway to her room, I found her bed still untouched from when we had arrived. I turned and ran into the living area. The bottle of Don Julio sat on top of the bar.

"Fuck!" I felt dizzy. She couldn't have gone far. Right? I

made a couple of steps toward the door and stopped. What was Leonora's last name?   Shit, I didn't even have her phone number. I saw the building she lived in but I had no idea which apartment was hers. I collapsed on the sofa and stared out at the sky emerging a steely blue behind the silhouetted shapes of the other mega hotels on the strip. A crane was swinging a huge girder with a tag line attached to it. The ironworkers were setting steel at sunrise.

I would return to Los Angeles, drive to her building in Venice and look for her. But I knew she would be gone. And what if I asked around? I could ask Timmy if he knew anything about her. Then I remembered that she'd met him on the sidewalk that day. She was passing the building as he entered. He invited her to the party, she accepted. Either way I knew that tracking her down would be futile. I got up from the sofa and went toward the window to watch the guys on the iron but I didn't make it.

CHAPTER 14
SPEEDBOLT

The only thing that kept me from falling twenty-seven stories was my left foot on a spud wrench stuck in a bolt-hole on a naked column. A certain death in the bitter December Chicago air. Standing on the inside flange on the column I could fall thirty feet and if I didn't hit a beam on the floor below it would still be a possible fatality. I was on the outside. And though the pay is good for a man of limited education or technological skills, most human beings on the planet are not mentally or physically equipped for such work. I am an ironworker. My position is connector, one of the men that climbs around gigantic jungle gyms to attach the pieces of steel that make up the skeletons of these skyscrapers. I relish this role. Like an eagle perched atop a sequoia, on a clear day I can see the curvature of our planet over lake Michigan. It appears mystical beyond the quiet calm that exists even in a steady biting wind.

Through the silence, a five thousand pound beam floats toward me as if it's on the end of a giant string from up in the clouds. I reach out to grab my end and ease it into place, inside the web of the column, I stab a spud to line up the holes and hold loosely but firmly. My partner, some fifty feet away on another column, signals the crane with his free hand, the beam runs uphill from my end until it swings into the web of his column. As the crane begins to lower the piece to level, I am already sticking a bolt on the opposite side of the lug from my wrench. It is a painful contortion to reach one gloved hand around this massive column, the other hand working the bolt through the holes in both beam and column. The belt weighs fifty pounds, everything a connector carries with him is made of steel; bags of bolts and various pointy and ingeniously crafted instruments. Hanging on to life by hooking one foot around the flange of the column, the other foot fighting to stay on the spud wrench. A yell over to my partner that I have a bolt made. He jumps up to sit on the beam straddling it like a steel Clydesdale. The connection of beam to column, of man and iron, the feeling is almost spiritual to me. It provides a temporary reprieve from the peril of hanging onto a half-inch thick flange of icy steel. A connector knows that you have to keep moving, using learned skill, guile and fearlessness to stay one step ahead of imminent danger. Accidents are inevitable, every ironworker has witnessed them, most have been the victim. Some are serious, some are the end. But a connector cannot think too much about things. Losing one's nerve can spell disaster, or worse, gain a reputation for being scared. The ultimate scarlet letter in this world. An ironworker does not consider himself a construction worker, but walks with the swagger and proud gait of an athlete. Until that day comes when injury and the pounding of the joints takes its toll.

I am a connector in a raising gang, a crew of five men that do the job of erecting the steel while another gang comes behind and sticks all of the bolts in the holes, does the welding, and covers the beams with sheets of corrugated steel that becomes the floor. A good raising gang is like poetry in motion. The foreman comes up with a plan on setting the steel in sequence, relays that plan to the connectors and the two hook-on guys. As a connector I am constant inertia, climbing around on this massive steel structure as effortlessly as a ring-tailed lemur navigates the high foliage of the rain forests.

I stuck four bolts in this connection, two in the top set of holes and another two bolts a couple holes down. I left open holes just beneath the top two for my spud wrenches. This connection was doubling straight out meaning that another beam would share the same exact set of bolts and holes in the column's web. This type of connection was always a dangerous proposition. I would use the pointy ends of my wrenches to line up the holes on the beam I sat on. There would be a moment when I would be sitting on this piece of steel that was not secure until a nut was placed on at least one of the bolts again. My partner Max slid down his column, walked across the beams below me and climbed the next column down the line.

The worst thing to hear in this situation, "It's walking!" Any number of things can happen to make a column at a double connection start to 'walk'. Until the floors are decked and the concrete is poured, the steel structure is alive like an organism. It breathes, it gives, it bows, it expands and contracts. In extreme elements it can be heard and even felt.

I was ready, bolts sticking true, wrench in hand and the end of the beam reached my hands with the delicate touch of a two and half ton feather. I pulled my end down and eased the lug over the waiting and naked bolts, the spud was perfectly lined up. Max had to go high on the other end for it to enter the web of the column. A gust of wind pulled his end out a good five feet then it slammed back into the column he was standing on. The building shook.

"It's fuckin' walking, guy," I said without shouting but loud enough to alert everyone. There was now an inch and a half gap between the lug of the beam I sat on and the web of the column. There was only a half thread of either bolt sticking past the other side of the web. Don't panic, hold that spud, I thought. Don't move a muscle. Out of my periphery I saw Max slide down his column and start across the beam below me, signaling the crane to put the piece back on the deck.

"Set that piece down and send the ball up to me," Max shouted like a general. "Can you stick a speed bolt?" he asked in the same breath as he neared the column.

"Max, don't walk underneath me guy…don't know how long I can hold this thing." The muscles in both of my forearms burning, both hands on one spud as the other one dangled loose, my legs shook.

Max reached the column where I was, looked up and said "I'm coming up behind ya guy, just hold on." He had to climb the column behind me to the bolted end of the beam I sat on, walk past center, grab the choker off the headache ball, sling it over the beam and let the crane take the weight of the beam off of the spud and my failing struggle. Making a ninety-degree turn underneath me to a beam running perpendicular, he had another hundred and fifty feet of top flange steel to traverse before he could scurry up to my level. The foreman and hook on guys were warning anyone else on the deck to steer clear.

I can't remember how far Max had gotten when the tip of my spud shot skyward for a flash then disappeared in the column's guillotine. I don't remember hitting the beam below and somersaulting to the deck another story down. Nor do I remember a three thousand pound beam that was cribbed up, rolling over onto my legs during the violent crash of the beam that I was on. I don't remember Max falling one story onto other staged steel only to act quickly, grab a choker, signal the crane over to where I was pinned, hook up to one end and remove me from the wreckage. I vaguely remember the twenty seven-story ride to the ground, it seemed like a morphine dream. Me and Max, covered in blood, he's on one knee, one hand on a choker, his other hand on my shoulder as I languished in the state of shock.

We rode a two-ton bundle of deck as a stretcher some four hundred feet to the ground. The crane lowering us at steady clip, I wondered if I was already dead and this was my last ride.

Max yelling for the last ten stories to a laborer on the ground to get a "fuckin" ambulance. That was the last fuzzy memory I had of that day. The next months would be half drug-induced dream, half nightmare as the drugs washed over me. I suffered a shattered femur, two broken ankles, three shattered ribs, a broken pelvis, a ruptured spleen, and a loss of three pints of blood. But it was the three fractures in my skull that scared the doctor's the most.

Max saved my life single handedly that day. The doctor said I would have bled to death in another five minutes. Max had a shattered ankle, four cracked ribs, a broken jaw and a concussion that kept him under observation in the hospital for a week. He later told me he only stuck around that long to hang out.

He had been my connecting partner, flying high on the steel for eight years. Max and I were best friends for that time. The endless competition and one-upmanship, visits to the emergency rooms, and a few close calls with death, words come up short in describing the bond. On the steel there was never much verbal communication between us, it was like telepathy. At full speed we were like moving parts in a high performance engine, hitting on all cylinders, yet completely silent except for the occasional clank of a spud wrench or the scraping sound of a slever bar being pulled from its holder.

CHAPTER 15
FUCKIN' SUICIDE KING

The metallic smell of blood came first, followed by a pounding in my head that made a noise like a bullet train running off the tracks. I lifted my head from the carpet, my cheek stuck to it. The sun was beaming through the windows and I was drenched in sweat. It took a full minute for my eyes to focus and the noise in my head to ebb. Staring out the window I saw the men working on the building. I got up and almost fell rushing to my room. The lights were on, the empty tray was still on top of the dresser. I ran to the bathroom and puked in the direction of the toilet. It was a gruesome convulsion. I tasted the undigested pills as they came back up. I heaved again, and again, eyes watering. Breaths came tough between expulsions.

I was in that bathroom for an hour. Dry heave, wash my face, then dry heave some more. I was sweating profusely, eyes watering so bad I was blind. I ran a cold shower and lasted five minutes. The bone-chilling water revived my wits. The events of the previous day reappeared to me, two of them brought desperation. There was the fifty thousand dollars left in play on a table from many hours ago. And a girl I knew nothing about walked off with four hundred and fifty thousand bucks from my room. The chips. She had to cash them out. That thought sent a sickness to my soul that was borderline suicidal. How could I have been so reckless? Should have followed my instinct right out the suite door to the casino once I saw Leonora was gone.

Those chips had to stay in the building. The large denominations had small GPS devices in them to thwart counterfeiters. She probably had no idea about this. I grabbed my phone, it was four in the afternoon and being unconscious for ten hours set off an alarm within my brain. And I needed my medicine. I chewed a handful of pills and washed them down with a Red Bull from the mini bar, and searched the pants pockets from the night before.

"Ed Donahue," he answered.

"Yeah Ed," my voice haggard. I cleared my throat and repeated, "yeah Ed, hey it's Mickey Fortunato..."

Interrupting me in the same cold tone, "I've been trying to get a hold of you for several hours, sir. The table is covered and waiting. Do you want to play the hand or surrender?"

Surrender? My heart fluttered like a flooded car trying to turn over.

"You can surrender the hand Mickey, forfeit half to the house and keep twenty five thousand. Or play the hand. This is a matter that needs to be resolved now or your wager will be forfeited," he said. The VIP status had been revoked.

"I'll be down in a minute. Hey Ed, do you know..." I was about to ask if he knew the whereabouts of my chips but he hung up on me. I knew the answer to my question and I was not in any shape to think about it at the moment. I grabbed fifty grand from the safe and exited the suite.

The table was as I left it at four in the morning. The casino was filling up behind me with tourists traipsing in from the pool or having just checked in, already drunk from the plane ride and anxious to blow their life's savings in the hopes of winning big. I could feel their anxiety as I passed them. Most of them knew the second they sat down that they would be at the ATM machine many times over the next few days.

Ed was sitting and a dealer awaited. We didn't exchange words. His hands were folded on the table as if expecting to be dealt into the next hand. He was waiting for me to lose. Without taking a seat, I grabbed the fifty grand from my pocket and placed it next to my original bet. "Cash played," I said indicating my wish to not exchange the bills for chips.

"Go ahead," Ed said to the dealer who was not Federica but a short and portly balding man. I didn't look at his nametag, just stared at the cash. "Count it out," Mr. Donahue ordered as he looked at me with pity.

It took the dealer several minutes to count it all. I had thoughts about surrendering half of my original bet. But the surly manner in which Donahue was dealing with me made me want to go on another run and stick it to him. Fuck Ed Donahue. Fuck the Venetian. Fuck this repulsive looking man about to deal me one card. And fuck that heartless bitch Leonora. Was that even her real name?

"Let me have the card face down," I said. Ed looked at me and gave the approval with a head nod to the dealer.

My card came face down as requested. The dealer used the six to flip his down card. It was a five. Fuck, had they planted it while I was passed out in a pool of my own blood for hours? The conspiracy theory was forming. My heart was racing.

The dealer drew a nine. Twenty. Suddenly my eleven which earlier looked a heavy favorite against the house's showing six, now appeared to be against the ropes needing a haymaker from me to pull this fight off in the final seconds. The dealer reached across the table and flipped my card.

King of hearts. The fuckin' suicide king. I started laughing as the weight of worry lifted suddenly and the world came back into perception as the dealer counted out a hundred thousand dollars in chips and slid them next to my mixed bet.

With two hundred grand on the table and another forty-five,

maybe fifty in the safe upstairs, "color me up," I said to the dealer.

"Sir, you already have the color, the table only has ten thousand dollar chips," the dealer said.

I stuffed the cash in my pockets, snatched the chips and went to walk away.

"Mr. Fortunato," Ed said in an almost apologetic tone.

I stopped and turned.

"If there is a situation with the special lady," he said, scribbling on the back of a business card, "Call this number in an hour or two."

I glanced at the card, slid it into my back pocket. "Appreciate it Ed. Easy come, easy go."

CHAPTER 16
JACKIE, I LOVE YOU

The painkillers were working to enhance my spirits as I cruised the speed limit on the way back to Los Angeles. With the windows up and the air conditioning on full blast, Warren Zevon sang to Carmelita about his heroin despair, the engine made a guttural purr beneath me.

I fueled up in Barstow and strolled the edge of the gas station lot where asphalt meets sand and caught a couple minutes of fresh desert air. Plotting my next move, I called the number on the back of the business card.

Just as I'd expected, Ed told me that my girlfriend cashed out the chips around the same time I left the table for the suite to cover the double down. They attempted to call me to verify this transaction but I did not answer either the suite's house phone nor my cell. She told them that I didn't feel good and that I was going to shower and sleep. I wanted to ask him how they could have let this happen. But I knew his explanation would be filled with holes. By the time he was explaining to me about casino policy and the fact that I'd elected to take the chips to the suite instead of leaving them with the casino I had already come to grips with this ironic twist of fate. I felt that I got what I deserved and that karma was a funny motherfucker.

I would still go looking for this girl from Venice beach. But I had other priorities at the moment. I needed to finish what I started, but luck had changed the scope of my crime spree. Another couple of banks should set me straight. Impulse struck once again.

The phone on the other end rang until it went straight to a voicemail with no greeting. I hung up and watched the white striped asphalt disappear beneath the beast. A minute later my phone rang. I slid it open without checking the screen. I knew who it was.

"Hey," she said.

It had only been a couple of days but it felt like a year since I found her note in the car. "I miss you Jackie."

"I fuckin' miss you too."

"I want to see you. What do you think?"

There was a pause. "I want to see you but Mick I'm lost. I don't know."

"Hey kid, I know the feeling. Maybe we're both lost. Come on, we'll go for a walk on the beach tonight, we'll sit in the sand and talk as the blackened ocean frightens us to our core," as I finished the sentence she let out a chuckle. My heart jumped.

"Yeah, all right, cool. I'll call later," she said. I could picture her smiling, biting her lip waiting for another word from me.

"See ya tonight kid," was all I could muster.

I wanted to talk to her all the way back to L.A. but she hung up. I was feeling warm inside at the prospect of seeing her. But I also saw through the false sense of well being induced by the pharmaceuticals. The gloom remained but I still had a lot to do. Knowing that Jackie was oblivious to my secret life clawed at the deepest part of my conscience and was becoming a burden to bear.

The loft was dark inside, the drapes were drawn and the cool air pumped steady from the vents. My fortress of solitude, my safe haven.

I walked to the safe and placed a quarter of a million cash and a dwindling supply of pills inside. The contents sitting there, I was betrothed to fate. I trudged up the stairs to my bed and laid down fully clothed, shoes still on, and slept without dreaming.

When I woke there was a single star visible through the skylight above me as my feet hung off of the bed. Checked my phone, it was two in the morning. No text messages, no missed calls. I walked down the stairs in a haze, phone in hand and opened the giant window. The sounds and smells of the city hit me. I called Jackie. She answered on the first ring.

"Sorry kid, I fell asleep. You still wanna take that walk?"

"For sure," was all she said.

"You by Liana's house?"

"I'll be in front when you get here."

"I'm on my way."

The waves rolled up onto the sand with a laziness as we walked in silence, stealing glances at each other. I knew we were hiding things from one another. It was the first time since we met that I felt she kept anything from me. It was not in my nature to think this way about a woman. I'd been searching for a girl that understood me. I believed that a good woman had nothing to hide. And my search for that combo seemed to end when I met Jackie. But her eyes were giving her away in the moonlight.

We found a stretch of sand a ways from the Santa Monica pier that was silent and dark. The sand was dry as the heat wave had reached the beach for the last week. We sat side by side, staring out into the invisible horizon.

"I'm on a strange trip right now Jackie."

"I know. I've known this for a while. Even before your trip back home. A distance growing between us."

Her words hit my heart and hung for a few seconds. "How so?"

"It's in your voice and in your body when you hold me. I know you have a lot on your plate and that you feel the weight of the world, but fuck, I'm dealin' with some shit too."

I looked her in her eyes, "Lay it on me kid, what's goin' on in that pretty mind of yours?"

With her shoulders raised, she let it go, "I'm fuckin' damaged goods Mickey," awash with tears, nose already running, "I'm broken. I'm fuckin' broken. You have a past that haunts you… and the odds are stacked and you're trying to reach the stars… I fuckin' love that about you and that drive…you to go for broke, failure be damned. I know that things didn't go as you'd expected in Chicago, but fuck, I got problems too…and I think it's better if we dealt with our own shit before we try to make a life together…"

Her words made me sober, struck true and everything became clear to me. I stayed silent, my arm grasped her from shoulder to hip, pulling her close. Her body tensed, did not dissolve into me as usual.

"I need to get right Mickey," she said through a sob that was building to uncontrollable weeping. She straightened up and pulled away, staring into the abysmal black of the Pacific. Her lips pursed to speak, but she froze. Her eye's welled with stifled tears that forced their way out, washing mascara down her cheeks.

I moved my hand up and massaged the small of her back. "What's goin' on baby," I said, resisting the urge to make eye contact, letting her vent. "Nothing's so bad to cry like this." I cupped her cheek with my hand and drew her to my chest. Her body convulsed on the brink of an all out cry.

"I gotta get clean, Mick…… I gotta get clean, I can't hide it from you any more. I know that your mother was sick like this and I didn't want to hide anything from you and……Oh Fuck!" Jackie exploded into a shower of emotion. My heart broke a thousand times in that moment. I melted. We were both strung out. So consumed in this venture, it was the first time I admitted it to myself. I'd intentionally ignored all the signs for selfish reasons.

I held her tight and began to rock her back and forth. "It's okay baby. It's okay, we're gonna be alright." Her tears were soaking through my t-shirt.

"I'm thinking about going home," her voice sounded weak. Her sobs waned, nose still runny.

"To New York?"

"I think it's best."

"For how long? Does your mother know?"

"Oh god no. I don't know if I could tell her, at least not any time soon. Liana is the only one…..and now you know.." She began crying again. "I'm so fucking sorry Mick, I'm fucking miserable. This whole scene here in LA is toxic for me and I've known it for a long time."

Her honesty had always been one of her more endearing qualities. I suppressed any urge to confess my own dark secrets though I'm sure it would've been cathartic. "Maybe you go to rehab, dry out for awhile before you go home. I've seen withdrawals kid and it ain't pretty. Your mother would know it's more than the flu."

She interrupted me, "Rehab? That shit costs a lot of money… money that I don't have."

"I'll pay for it Jackie. Don't even worry about it."

"Mick, you don't have that kind of money. I know that you are struggling to try and make this movie and trying to figure shit out for yourself. I'll just go home, fuck, maybe I'll come clean to my mom about everything," Jackie said with conviction as she wiped the tears from her face with the sleeve of her hoodie and lit a cigarette.

"Listen, don't worry about the money. I'm pretty close to

getting things lined up. I'd been thinking about putting it on hold anyways. Go to a rehab place for a few weeks at least."

"Mickey, they cost anywhere from twenty to fifty thousand dollars," she said with a hopeless look in her eyes. But I could tell that she really wanted this option.

It would set me back, but my guilt made this an easy decision. I knew the nature of the beast that lived within her. Getting clean would be the easiest part if she had professional help in a supportive environment. The hard part would be staying clean. My own addiction was tearing me apart but I had confidence I could slay my demons when the time came.

"So when do you want to go?" I said.

"Now, but we have to figure it out. Right? Are you sure you have the money for this? God, I can't believe we're actually having this conversation. I think I'm gonna be sick," she said.

"Do you want to come home with me tonight? We can find a place tomorrow and figure everything out," I said this, afraid that witnessing her being dope sick, my guilt would get the best of me and I'd tell her everything. She deserved honesty but the truth would overwhelm her.

"I don't want you to see me like this."

"Like what?" I continued against my own wishes that she go to Liana's house. "Jackie, I love you." It was the first time I'd said those words to her.

She stared at me with sad eyes, desperate and hollow, not alive and full of wonder like they used to be. "I fuckin' love you too," she said and buried her head in my chest and held tight as if it would be the last time. I held her shaking body for a long time before dropping her off at Liana's house in Santa Monica.

CHAPTER 17
ANGEL WITH A DIRTY FACE

O n the way back to my loft I'd thought about stopping by the building where Leonora lived. It was only a few miles from where I dropped Jackie off. But my body was giving out. I could barely keep my eyes open as I drove the 10 east. I was afraid to sleep, crash through an entire day. I could not afford to do that if I was going to make this movie happen.

I made a mental list as I drove. I had to track down this girl that walked away with my money. That task was fraught with headaches. She could call the police if I tried to coerce her to do the right thing and give me my fuckin' money. Leaning on her would be a tricky proposition too. Before finding out about Jackie being a junkie I was even thinking of letting the whole thing go. I was strangely compelled to leave that story as is, open-ended. Sure, Leonora saw those chips on the dresser and saw an opportunity. Maybe it was easier for me to reconcile the theft after the relief I felt when I won that hand of blackjack. My father once told me that I deserved to get my bike stolen because I left it on the sidewalk. Twenty-five years later I left four hundred and fifty thousand dollars out in the open in a Vegas suite with a girl I'd met the same day. Money won from money I stole from two banks. Maybe the universe was trying to tell me something.

I had to get Jackie to rehab. I had to plan my next heist in the event that Leonora couldn't be found. Jackie first. Leonora second. Case another bank third. But I found myself thinking that I really needed to take a few days to gather myself. I was exhausted. The toxicity of my blood had me jittery, my organs were redlining and I knew it. I was treating major nosebleeds like the sniffles. My eyes were constantly stinging and red and I had to douse them with Visine every couple of hours. I was chewing fifty or sixty pills a day and I started to wonder if I should check myself into rehab along with Jackie. Maybe they'd have some sort of two for one discount. But I told myself I could cut back. I knew where this habit was leading. I was scared of being sick, especially quitting at this point. With the amount I was taking I would surely degrade into a mess of shitting and puking, sweating and shivering on the cusp of death for at least a week. Didn't have time for that. I would ride it out until I had a couple months to disappear from the world, crawl into the shadows, and heal out of sight like a wounded animal.

When I arrived back at my place I shut the windows and closed the drapes. I popped a couple of Xanax and took a long hot shower. I tried calling Jackie but she didn't answer. I tried not to picture her in whatever state she might be in. I was haunted with visions of her nodding in a stupefied heroin fog. I started crying and once I started there was nothing the Xanax could do to calm me down. I hadn't wept like that since I was a scared little kid in a dark motel room wondering if I'd ever see my father again. I felt the same cold and lonely pangs in that moment thinking about Jackie. I couldn't get over the fact that I didn't figure out earlier on that she was so fucked up. But then again, drug addicts become terrific liars. I was becoming one of those.

I shot a text to Jackie.

"No matter what happens in this life I will never look at you any different than when I first kissed you. I will hold you when you need to be held. Care for you when you are sick. Listen to you when you need to talk. This is a promise I will take to my grave. It's gonna get worse before it gets better but in the end you will be stronger. It won't be easy but do not worry, I'm in this thing all the way with you. I'll see you in my dreams tonight. Call me tomorrow. Don't worry about the money. I love you baby."

I pushed send and blackness washed over me as my mind finally shut down, the anti-anxiety drugs kicked into high gear. I was out and slept the sleep of a dead man.

When I finally woke up the sheets were soaking wet and I was covered in sweat. It was nighttime, again I could see that single star through the skylight. Checked my phone for the time but the battery was dead. I ran downstairs to turn the TV on to see what time it was, or what day it was for that matter. My legs were weak and my head was pounding when I drew the drapes and opened the window. I didn't need to look at the television to know that I'd slept for at least a day. The empty streets and sidewalks below, and the cool night temperature gave it away. I turned and glanced at the TV, which was on the guide channel. Two thirty a.m.

I went to the fridge, there was only beer and bottled water and a frozen pizza. I slammed two of the waters and turned on the oven to cook the pizza, then ran to grab my phone and the charger and relocated to the sofa. I stared at the tube and started scrolling down the channels. I settled on ESPN SportsCenter, any visual stimuli to numb the brain. I watched without paying attention for several minutes before my phone turned on. No missed calls. No messages. My heart sank so I took my medicine and felt my nerves calm within minutes. By the time the pizza was cooked my body was euphoric, my brain manic, I was not hungry but I forced myself to eat. I was losing weight by the day, my clothes were hanging from my body. Though I'd just slept for nearly an entire day I knew I was running on empty. After zoning out for an hour on the sofa I decided to take a drive.

With the windows down and a mix that Jackie made me playing old R&B songs, I drove down Wilshire making my way toward the beach. I didn't have a plan but this was the direction I was compelled to go, waiting for an idea to come into focus. But there was no focus in my brain, only blissful mayhem. Baby Huey was singing about 'Hard Times' when I found myself making a turn towards Liana's house. I messaged Jackie and told her I wanted to see her.

By the time I pulled up in front of the house she still hadn't messaged me back. I called. She answered on the first ring. Her voice was groggy.

"Mickey," dragging the word through an opiate mire. "Where have you been."

"How you feelin' kid?" But I already knew how she felt. I knew what she probably looked like right now. A wreck.

"I'm not well baby," the words still slurred. "But I need you, I need you to hold me. I need to hear your voice tell one of your stories..."

I suddenly regretted being there. On one hand I promised her that I'd do anything to help her. On the other hand I was having a premonition about where our two drug-addled minds and longing for each other's company might lead the both of us. "I'm outside kid. Why don't we take a ride, get a bite to eat. You hungry?"

"I'm not hungry Mick, I just want you to hold me. You're outside?" Her voice raspy and soft.

"Right out front."

"Okay, gimme a couple minutes. You'll wait for me won't you Mick?"

"Of course I will Jackie."

As I was waiting a cop slowed to take a look at me sitting in the car with my headlights running. I was double parked on Fourth Street at four in the morning, fifteen painkillers in my pants pocket with another twenty circulating through my veins. I was waiting for my girlfriend to emerge from this building, who was probably high on heroin and would probably have drugs on her person. This cop was for sure going to make another pass after he ran my plates. "Just get the fuck outta here guy," I said to myself. Right then Jackie emerged from the building wearing the same dirty hoodie from the beach the other night. She jumped in.

Neither of us said anything as I took off in a hurry trying not to squeal my tires. Too late, my foot sank the gas pedal as I decided to roll the dice and get to the 10 before that lifeguard with a badge circled around. I was tearing through Santa Monica as if I was being chased and Jackie said nothing.

I eased up once we were on the expressway for a minute or two, not a single car in the rearview.

"Where are we going?" She broke the silence.

"I really didn't have a plan to be honest with you," I said as I looked over, passing streetlights illuminating her through the passenger window every few seconds. It started to rain. She had the hood over her head. Her Roman nose and full lips were visible in profile. Her eyes were hidden. I reached over and pushed the hood back off of her head. She turned and looked at me. Her eyes were bloodshot and tired, withdrawn. Tears welled up in mine. My eyes focused back on the rain soaked road. It was really coming down now as if the world was feeling the anguish of the two lost souls in the car.

I exited at La Cienega and went north to Wilshire to a twenty-four hour Ralph's. We pulled into the underground garage and out of the downpour.

"Come on, we'll stock up on anything you want. Take a bunch of creature comforts back to the loft and lock the door, forget about the world for a day or three, whatever it takes," I said without knowing what I was doing. I wanted my heart to feel something sad, I felt the need to see Jackie in shambles. Maybe then I would see the next chapter of my life unfold. Maybe a dose of clarity would stop me from doing what I was doing.

"I'll just wait here for you."

"Alright. Want do you want," knowing the answer would be nothing as she could probably only think of the shame of the situation and food isn't even a thought to her.

She did not answer. She did not even look at me as she pulled the hood back over her head and lit a cigarette. I went into the store alone, spent all of ten minutes filling a cart in a hurry with junk food and pop. As I was grabbing things in rapid fashion a vision appeared to me. Jackie and me shacking up, watching movies and smoking weed. Making love so much we would forget to dance with the devil and indulge our weaknesses. Maybe we could love each other through withdrawals. I knew it was just those pills giving me optimistic delusions.

I approached my car pushing the shopping cart. I could not see Jackie's silhouette through the window that was now rolled up. I almost snapped as I went for the car.

"Hey," her voice coming from behind me. She was smoking another cigarette, sitting against the wall on the pavement. With her hoodie and ripped blue jeans and Vans skateboard shoes she looked like a teenaged runaway straight out of an 80's movie. I was relieved to see she had not ditched me. She remained against the wall, smoking while I loaded the groceries into the car.

"Are you comin' with me or are you gonna hang out in this parking lot all day like an angel with a dirty face," It was a reference to a James Cagney movie that I watched with my father when I was a kid. Half of a smile crossed my face as I said it.

She gave a weak giggle and rose to her feet and flicked the butt. "That's funny," she said getting into the car.

I got in and cranked the ignition. "What's so funny?" I leaned over, my face in front of hers. She kissed me softly.

"Angel with a dirty face. I like that," she said.

We drove back to my loft in the rain. Wilson Pickett on the speakers singing a great version of 'Hey Joe'. Jackie loved Hendrix but always liked this version better. I was thinking about Leonora while that song played for some reason. I was thinking that maybe her conscience would get the best of her and she'd return my money without me having to hunt her down. And though stranger things had happened to me in this lifetime, her showing up at my door, bag of money in hand, was nothing but a dream. Life was never that easy.

CHAPTER 18
LIQUID PEACE

We took turns taking showers, Jackie going first. When I emerged from the bathroom the smell of eggs and onions wafted through the loft. Jackie was standing at the stove working a frying pan wearing only panties and a bra. It had been less than a week since I'd seen her naked, but it was obvious that she hadn't eaten much in that time. Standing there with a cigarette's smoke rising from an ashtray on the counter she said, "breakfast burritos?" It was our favorite thing to eat no matter the time of day. I moved in behind her as she worked the spatula through the heap of eggs, chopped ham, cheese, and onions. I put my hands on her shoulders, swept her still damp hair to one side and started planting small wet kisses on her neck. Our bodies drew close, my half erection pressed through the wet towel into her ass cheek that had lost some plump. Her free hand reached up to touch the side of my face. I noticed her feet and a vision of my mother flashed through my head, Jackie had been shooting junk between her toes to conceal her habit.

"Don't stare at my feet. Don't make me feel worse than I already do." Her vulnerability made me want to confess everything.

"I'm not staring at your feet, kid. I'm watching you slow cook the shit out of these eggs. Is the burner even on?" I moved my hand down to cup her ass. She gave me the best smile she could summon.

"I don't feel well," she said.

I was wondering how much she was using and how often. I wanted to have this conversation. The need to hear details was selfish and I knew it. Her shame was evident but my curiosity came from wanting to divulge my personal demons. But I didn't. I rationalized this, telling myself that she'd worry like hell if she knew I was swallowing a month's worth of prescription pain pills on a daily basis. A month's supply for someone with serious injuries or pain. I started out that way, years ago. But my injuries healed and a new pain led me to where I stood at that moment. I stared at the track marks on my twenty-one year old girlfriend's foot. We were both in the throes of being dopesick and for the first time since realizing the pills were a serious problem, I felt comforted in knowing that I was not alone.

I had always wondered what was going through my mother's mind when I'd see her nodding off on the sofa or on the bed. She would catch me staring at her and she'd say, "Mommy doesn't feel well." The only memories I have of my mother sporting a smile of true joy was when she didn't feel well.

Talking to Jackie as I ate her cooking, we'd decided to spend a couple of days together, laying low, rekindling our romance before she went off to get better. It was the plan of two junkies, doomed to be reworked.

It had been over twenty-five years since I had witnessed someone injecting heroin. The memories rushed back to me with horrifying speed once I saw Jackie's eyes roll back into her head. Her body went limp with a gasp of exhaled breath in the dim light of my loft. She was alone now, off in her own euphoria. I carried her from the sofa up to my bed. She could barely speak as I laid her down under the skylight. There was no star shining through that night as raindrops hit the thick glass without making a sound. I sat on the edge of the bed and she rolled away from me without a mumbled word. I rubbed her back for a couple of minutes then went back to the sofa where the TV was on, volume turned all the way down. Humphrey Bogart in 'The Petrified Forest' was playing. Jackie's purse was on the coffee table next to the needle that I'd grabbed when she'd almost dropped it on the floor in her stupor.

I had only taken about ten pills since I'd picked Jackie up, about eighteen hours ago. We'd smoked a couple of joints while we laid around watching TV and that slowed my body some from getting the jitters. Jackie was procrastinating her fixes as well.

In the same way that I jumped into my first bank job without a plan, I began the ritual that I'd seen so many times in my childhood. I had watched every step that Jackie took because I wanted to experience this world with her. I was shaking as I searched her purse and found a bindle that contained several little balloons. My mother used powder heroin that was brown, sometimes white. That was the late seventies and early eighties. The stuff that Jackie was using looked like little balls of asphalt. Black tar heroin she said with shame in her voice when I asked her about it. I had no idea how much to put in the spoon to melt down. I should have been scared at not knowing this detail. I was not. Disgusted and curious at the same time, I methodically mimicked Jackie's steps. I'd thought about sterilizing the tip of the syringe but it was such a fine tip I wasn't sure if it would be ruined. I remembered the needle my mother used as being much larger. But then again, memories from childhood had a way of becoming distorted in that way. Everything was bigger, colors were brighter, sugar tasted sweeter.

I took the skittle-sized ball of sticky dope from the balloon and placed it in the spoon followed by a capful of water. My hand was shaking so much now that I leaned the edge of the spoon off of the coffee table to hold the flame from the lighter underneath to dissolve the heroin. I held the handle flat against the wood with one hand and worked the lighter with the other until there was nothing but murky water in the spoon. It smelled like vinegar. I set the lighter down and used that hand to steady my wrist to put the spoon flat on top of the table. Not wanting to spill any, I grabbed the Q-tip cotton, tore the little ball off and dropped it into the dose. I depressed the plunger all the way down before sticking it into the cotton to draw my first fix of heroin into Jackie's needle. My hand steadied, a calm came over me once the syringe sat in front of me on the coffee table. I stared at it. I didn't know why, but I wanted to feel what Jackie was feeling. I knew that pain pills were derived from the same substances as heroin and morphine, just synthetic. But I knew that injecting heroin was on another level altogether.

I envisioned Jackie emerging from her high and finding me on the sofa, needle dangling from my arm, eyes glazed over, regurgitated bile dried on my cold lips. It seemed romantic in the sickest way. Once this drug grabbed someone's soul there were two ultimate outcomes. Prison or an early grave, and many times both. I didn't think about tying off my arm with a belt. I was vascular, my veins needed no constricting of blood flow to bulge my skin. Without another thought, I stuck the needle in the large vein in the crook of my left arm and pressed the plunger down.

My life flashed before my eyes. I saw my mother getting fucked in the ass while she sucked another guy's dick. I saw another man beating the shit out of Dominic at four years old with huge fists. Punches meant for a man, not a boy. I saw Jackie angelic, riding me as her long blonde hair glowed radiant and brilliant around her serene youthful visage. I saw my father's body, mangled and bloodied in a rice patty in Vietnam. I became sick within seconds of ingesting the dope and did not make it three steps before projectile vomiting all over the floor. Then my world came to a place I'd only dreamed about. I collapsed back into the sofa and forgot about the mess on the floor as a warmth and comfort I'd never experienced in my life washed over me. I wanted to cry tears of joy but I was paralyzed. I wanted to die like this.

One day turned into two, and two days turned into two weeks. During that time we left my loft only to gather more supplies for the trip we were on together. Cigarettes and more drugs; weed, heroin and hash. After the first couple of days there was no talk of Jackie going to rehab. When we were awake and had the energy to talk, we spoke of the sadness in our pasts and deluded each other with plans for a future together. But no talk of getting out of this spiral. We seemed to be on a suicide mission as our tolerance quickly grew. I'd all but forgotten about Leonora every time I felt that needle deliver that liquid peace. Jackie acted as if this was the only way she'd ever want to be. My heart shattered whenever I came down. So we stayed high.

One day I woke from a nod and she was gone. And so were the drugs. Her phone was disconnected. I ate twenty pills. It only made me stop sweating for a few hours. I called L and asked him for the strong ones. He said no problem, but I'd have to pay fifty bucks a pill, even in quantity. The promo sale was over. I didn't care. I had to go forward and hope that a plan would appear. I had not an ounce of clarity in my brain at the time and didn't know if I had it in me to rob another bank and I couldn't imagine myself finding Leonora and confronting her. I could not look at myself. A glance in the mirror would tell me the truth. In the last three weeks I had gone from Robin Hood, trying to help others realize dreams, to rock-bottom junkie, my mother's offspring. I was a fuckin' wreck and thoughts of suicide by overdose were becoming constant. I had never felt so desperate as when I'd realized Jackie was gone.

CHAPTER 19
FATBURGER

"I got that demonstration fo ya, homeboy," L said on the other end of the phone. "Whenever is good for you, but it's gotta be today. Headed outta town, you feel me?"

"No sweat, guy. I can come now. Fatburger on Figueroa. Cool with you?"

"By USC? Yeah that's cool. I got a hundred on the game today, can you cover that action?" He said.

"Not a problem man. I'll be there in a half hour," I said, knowing that I'd need a couple minutes to pull myself together. I thought it ironic that I'd be ashamed to see my drug dealer in any state.

"Bet," and the phone clicked.

I was about to hand over five grand for a hundred pills. My bankroll had taken a beating in the last couple of weeks, I had less than two hundred grand left. I grabbed the money from the safe and popped the last handful of pills in my stash. I made up my mind to go looking for Leonora once I replenished my supply and got myself right.

There were two black and whites parked next to the Fatburger so I cruised through the lot and exited onto an adjacent street. I shot a text to L and told him we should pick another spot.

My phone rang. "Hey man, it ain't no thang. Just a coupla' pigs eating lunch, that's all it is home slice," L said sounding irritated by my caution.

"Guy, just hang cool and text me when they're gone, I'll slide through then."

"I got things to do my man, be here in two minutes or I bounce." I didn't feel good about it but I was desperate for what he had.

I parked on the street, out of sight from the cop cars, checked myself in the mirror, popped my sunglasses on, and walked the half block to the restaurant. Though the skies were dark with rain clouds I saw my reflection in the glass as I was opening the door to the burger joint. Needed to take the shades off. If these cops had seen my photo in the station or something that had come over the wire, I would be wearing shades in them. I had the same feeling walking into Fatburger as I'd had in the Chase.

L had his back to the wall in a booth by the restrooms. The police were in the next booth closer to the door. We would be actors in a scene. I walked over to L, the cops seemed to be consumed while they ate. My dealer was dressed business casual, like he stepped from the cubicle to have a burger, not sell five grand worth of Oxycontin to a bank robber.

"This stuff will kill you Larry," I said to L as I approached the booth where he sat eating a huge greasy burger and fries.

"The things we enjoy most in life always seem to be the biggest killers. You gonna join me my man?" L said falling right in step as the improvisation commenced.

"Yeah, I guess I'll sit with you and work towards arteriosclerosis," I said as I stole a glance at one of the cops that was staring at me as he chewed his food. It was a hard stare. He was a young officer, white, late twenties, crew cut, athletic jaw, and biceps stretching his shirtsleeves. His partner, a Latino guy in his mid-thirties, same physical characteristics only darker skin and rounded face, paid no mind and texted on his phone.

I turned away and walked to the register and ordered. Pulled out my phone to act busy. The whole time I was clocking the officers, trying to 'be cool'. The drugs had really done a number on my nerves. Paranoia was almost palpable.

My order came up, burger, fries and a large drink. I slid into the booth across from L. There was no conversation coming from the cop's booth, only some indecipherable calls and code coming in over their radios. I wanted their lunch break to be abbreviated by an emergency call.

"Do you know about this street right outside, Figueroa?" L asked me in between small bites of his gigantic burger.

"I know that it's a long fuckin' street. Runs from what, Gardena to Chinatown? That's gotta be twenty miles," I left an invitation for L to expound, waste time and lose the cop's attention if they were paying any.

"Figueroa actually runs from Pasadena to Long Beach."

"I'll give you Long Beach. Never gone that far south, besides the freeway. Thought Fig ended at Chinatown."

"It picks back up by Dodger Stadium, runs north a ways from there," L said taking another bite.

"That's pretty interesting. So what, you wanted me to know that Figueroa is just another long winding street in the greater Los Angeles area that starts and stops at random places?" We were like old friends busting balls for no good reason. And no good material.

"No man, it was named for General Jose Figueroa, a Mexican General turned governor of California...before it was a U.S. state."

"And what was so special about this Mexican General to name a major thoroughfare in his honor."

"He fought to take back the Catholic missions in California, return that shit to the natives. See, back then California was property of Mexico, but Spain was still running the show. Franciscan priests ran the missions like towns. The church owned everything, the buildings, the farms, stores that sold supplies to the families living in the missions. These people were the native Americans in the area, some with mixed blood. Meztisos. Figueroa was Meztizo."

"Didn't know you were such a history buff, Larry?"

"Point being, shit I don't know how to get straight to my point without going into a fuckin dissertation, but it all goes back to the Catholic Church. That big, corrupt, powerful company from Italy." L was saying this argumentatively to make the cops want to take their food and leave.

"I don't know about this Figueroa dude but I know what you're saying about the Catholic Church. They own more land on this planet that any single land owner," I said dragging this pointless trivia on. I had noticed that L had not touched his drink, same as the time I met him in the McDonalds. "To be continued, I'll be back," I said as I got out of the booth to go to the restroom. I wanted to count out the cash and have it handy, make the exchange under the table. I was starting to feel clammy and the nausea was making it hard for me to continue playing this charade. All the while, the two cops could be playing possum, waiting for either L or me to give them a reason. I had no idea about L's status with the law.

In the restroom there was one stall and one urinal, no lock on the door. I took the stall and sat down on the toilet not even checking for filth on the seat. I was disgusted at my own actions more and more these days. As I was fleshing out the bills I heard someone enter the restroom. The squeak of heavy rubber soles told me it was one of the officers. I saw his shoes under the partition as he pulled up to the urinal and unzipped. I flushed to drown out the sound of me undoing my belt buckle and unzipping my pants, tucked the money away, make it appear I was doing what this stall was here for in case the officer got a peak inside.

I heard something come over the radio, codes and names that

meant nothing to me. He zipped up and rushed out. I finished counting out the five grand, put it into my front right pocket, put the rest of my roll into the left. I went back into the restaurant.

The cops were still there, one was returning from the counter with a refill on his drink while the other one on his cell. I sat back down. L was drinking from the straw and I took that to mean he'd already made the switch.

"I think I'm gonna get outta here, get back to the office in time to stop and talk to that sexy new security guard at the front desk," L said as he crumpled up the wrapper from his burger with his right hand.

I pulled the cash from my pocket with my right hand and the switch was done in one second. "Alright man, we'll finish this bullshit history lesson some other time," I said. I still had a full tray of food to eat if I wanted to play this thing to the hilt. I was sick at the thought of eating that greasy food, with nothing to wash it down with unless I emptied the pills out and got a refill. My back to the cops, I started to wolf down the burger, trying to concentrate on how much better I'd feel once I could get to my car and chew a handful of medicine.

I finished half the burger and crushed the remainder in the wrappers. Wearing a look of self-disgust, I glanced at the young white cop. He was not looking as a call was coming over his radio. I grabbed the cup from the tray as I was dumping the remnants of my half eaten lunch into the trash and the cup felt completely empty. A fire rushed through my body as I hurried for the door.

"Hey!" I heard one of the cops yell as the door was closing behind me. I continued walking. It was beginning to rain when I heard the officer again, this time the voice was outside of the restaurant. I wanted to run. But I didn't. My mind raced and my heart stopped, a ringing in my ears seemed to drown out the noises of the cars sloshing by on Figueroa. I didn't turn as he spoke again.

"Hey buddy, you forgot your phone," he said as I stood there frozen for a second before I could process what he was saying. But the only thing I could think of at the moment was that there were no drugs in this cup and I'd just been ripped off for five grand. And here was the cop that looked straight out of central casting for Johnny Utah in full LAPD regalia handing me my phone that I'd left on the table. The look on my face must've made him wonder when I turned and made a stride to meet him half way in the rain.

"Thanks man, I appreciate it," I said as I grabbed the phone from his outstretched hand. For a split second I'd felt as if he was going to slap the cuffs on me. But he just turned and jogged back into the Fatburger. The rain became a downpour so I started to run toward my car, mid stride I popped the top off the cup. Empty. I tossed the cup into the street as I jumped into the SRT.

I called L. No answer. Sent a text as I drove with my knees on the rain soaked streets back to my loft. No returned message.

Motherfucker.

CHAPTER 20
VING RHAMES

At the loft I changed out of my wet clothes and tried Jackie. No answer. Texted her, no reply. I was feeling the walls of my dark and dank loft closing in on me. It was accelerating the need to medicate. I checked the safe to see if there were any stray pills in there. Nothing. I searched through all of the pockets of pants unwashed and jackets in the closet. There were two pills in the bottom of an inside pocket of one of my leather jackets. I chewed them up and washed the dust down with a beer. Followed by another.

I thought about calling Timmy. He was the only person I could think of that might be able to procure drugs. He rarely even smoked weed, he was just a binge drinker. And he knew nothing of my secrets. I nixed that idea out of the last bits of shame I possessed. Threw on some warm-ups, a pair of waterproof steel-toed Lugs, an Adidas pullover hoodie and went walking in the direction where I'd first met L. In the time that had passed since our first meeting, I'd only walked that stretch a few times. Each time I'd been accosted by street peddlers much the same way that I'd met L. The others were less slick. They'd simply come up to me on the sidewalk and ask me what I was looking for. Desperate now, I was looking for such a fool. It takes one to know one, I guess. My father's words echoed through my mind as I looked for a new drug dealer in the middle of daytime downtown Los Angeles. Drugs made people weak and stupid. Maybe L saw my weakness and decided I was an easy mark, knowing I wouldn't check the cup with the eyes of the law on my back. He was slick. Again I felt responsible for getting ripped off. If the world was conspiring to leave me busted and broke I was making its task an easy one.

It was a steady drizzle. My clothes were saturated by the time I reached the intersection of Fifth and Spring. Along the way I'd ducked into every doorway to check my phone. No messages, no calls. Each duck-in it was either the same time as the last or one minute later. I'd run it down, calling L first then Jackie. No answers. The texts remained out there in the ether.

I walked to the Rite Aid on Broadway and bought a pack of Parliament Lights, checked the phone once more and turned west on Fifth Street and headed to the Rosslyn Hotel. The Rosslyn was notorious for being sort of a halfway-house rent-by-the-week drug dispensary. I went there and ducked out of the rain under the overhang and lit a cigarette. An old man appeared from the doorway leading into the hotel. He was not a bellhop.

"Say man, can I bum one of them squares," he said with a toothless smile. His face was sunken and weathered but his clothes were clean, his wingtips polished.

Cigarette dangling from my lips, I retrieved the pack from my pants pocket and handed it to him, "take two if you want," I said staring out into the street, scanning for prospective dealers. I felt his eyes looking me over.

"Thanks young man, that's mighty kind of you," he said. His manner was over-the-top polite, like a sweet old man that lived on the block. "So what you lookin' for today, something in a bottle or you lookin' for somethin' in a balloon?" Salvation.

Told him I needed both. The thought of shooting heroin seemed to calm my nerves, but wanted to see if I could steady myself with pills first. I gave him my phone number. He said someone would text me in a few minutes about the when and the where. He disappeared back into the hotel. He didn't even light one of the cigarettes that he bummed. I never saw him again.

I jogged the long city block back to my place to wait for the text and to have only the money needed on my person. A text popped up on the cell as I was putting another set of dry clothes on. It was only a phone number. I dialed it.

"So here's the deal man. We meet at Pershing Square, I check you out, if everything's cool, you ain't five-o, then we'll talk. Tell me what you wearin'," the voice sounded similar to L's only with more bass. I was picturing Ving Rhames on the other end of the line.

I thought real quick about the question and decided to put the wet pullover back on. Maybe he had already seen me wandering about earlier. Even if I had the time I wouldn't have been able to think clearly. I was in a bad way. "I'll be wearing an Adidas jacket, stripes down the sleeves." He hung up. I put on some dry pants and the pullover, grabbed another two grand from my dwindling stash and went back out into the dreary streets to be sized up by Ving Rhames in Pershing Square. I pounded another two beers before leaving hoping I was about to get stronger.

On sunny days the Square, named after General "Blackjack" Pershing, was a place where the homeless lounged on benches side-by-side with 9-to-fivers wearing suits off the rack. No such culture clashes on this day. It was as gray as any day I could remember during my time in Los Angeles. The rain felt greasy on the pavement as I crossed streets mid-block, reckless moves.

I crossed Sixth Street and climbed the few elongated steps to the square and spotted what had to be Mr. Rhames. He was seated on a bench across the square and had an umbrella down close to his head, only his chin visible. I approached.   Even seated, this man was huge. He wore creased slacks that came down over cowboy boots and a duster over a suit coat. Everything from his skin to his umbrella, black as night. Boots looked as if they hadn't been touched by a single drop of rain. Was I hallucinating?

He did not look up as I sat on the wet concrete bench ten feet from him. He stood and began to walk toward Hill Street. He was halfway across the square when I decided to follow. It had to be him. I strode swiftly but gave a wide berth. "say my man," I said to him a good twenty feet away. He kept walking. "Say my man, you got the time?" I did not know what to say.

He stopped and looked at me for the first time. He wore round-framed glasses too small for his face that was dominated by a furrowed brow overhanging menacing eyes. A three-inch scar running from his right earlobe to his mouth. "walk with me if you wanna know the time, son." He collapsed the umbrella and I followed him down the stairs to the subway station at Fifth and Hill. Halfway down the stairs he stopped and said, "Look here man, I know you ain't the police, but you look small time and I deal in weight, feel me?" If you lookin' to cop for a day or two then I'm not the guy, you dig?"

"I dig, but you got me all wrong my man. I got you covered with whatever you got," I said.

He let out a single chuckle and said, "This cat right here said he got me covered. You a funny ma'fucka' man." He continued down the stairs. I followed. When we reached the platform it was completely empty except for an elderly Asian woman wearing a trash liner as a poncho at the ticket machine. We strolled toward the furthest corner of the platform. "so what's it gonna be, pills, powder, sticky? Talk to me brotha," his deep velvet voice smoothed the level of menace in his presence.

I wanted heroin. But I couldn't bring myself to utter the words. "Painkillers. What can you get?"

"Shiiieeet, I get you whatever you fuckin' want. You want Oxy's, you want Vicodin, you want straight morphine pills, Percs, I got em. I seen you around man, I figured you for a pill-popper," he said with smirk.

I was sick with the admonishment. "Whatever man. How much for the Oxy's?"

"That depends on what you want. I got tens, twenty's, fifty's and eighty's. Sell by the box. Five hundred pills. On the corner they gon' run ya a buck a milligram. By the box I sell them at eighty cents on the dollar. How's your math skills fella?"

I was getting pretty sick but the numbers came quickly. "I'll take the fifty's. When can you make it happen?"

"Well I ain't got the shit on me," he said as a train was pulling up.

He pulled a cell phone out of his jacket pocket and flipped it open and sent a text message. The Asian woman got on the train and it left. "Like I was saying man, I got your number, wait for a text message. You got that kind of scratch, huh? Cuz if you bull-shittin' you a marked man."

I must've looked pretty weak for him to keep driving the point home. "Twenty large. Like I said, I got you covered my man."

"I ain't yo man, but I'm yo man. You dig, homeboy?" He reached into his pocket and handed me a small envelope, the type you might get from a hardware store with a copy of a key just cut. He walked away as if I was not there.

I waited until he disappeared up the stairwell to the street and checked the envelope on the way up. It was a small piece of paper folded into a square. I jogged back to the loft, my heart racing thinking about what was inside. I was not feeling good about the cryptic nature of the last hour and a half. The old man with no teeth. The text messages. Ving Rhames and his conde-scending ways. But as soon as I locked the deadbolt behind me I felt excited at the prospect of feeling better. Inside the folded square of paper was a single pill. A fifty-milligram Oxycontin. I had never taken one but I knew a girl that used to crush them up and snort them. These pills went for as much as sixty dollars on the street.

In my rain soaked clothes I went to the closet and grabbed an old broad head bull pin from my ironworking belt. I placed the single pill on the marble topped counter and crushed it into dust. Then I used a butter knife to scrape the remnants off the head of the steel spike. My heart sank as I realized I had no idea what I was doing. The pill was smashed but the coating seemed to make the dust not of snorting quality. I licked my finger and dipped it into the crushed up mess. It took me five swabs until every grain was in my mouth. I grabbed a beer from the fridge and washed the dust down, making sure that the entire pill was ingested. I was dope sick, on the verge of panic, thinking it would be some time until Ving Rhames delivered. A ray of hope appeared. It was a message on my phone.

My hands shook as I slid the phone open. My heart felt as if it would explode as I read the message. "WHAT'S YOUR ADDRESS?" It read. I felt like I didn't have a choice. I replied, "610 s. Main. PH205".

No reply. I waited. After five minutes I started to feel somewhat composed. Either the drugs were finally working or I was optimistic about drugs being delivered to my door, but the apprehension and paranoia faded fast. I grabbed twenty grand, wrapped it in tin foil and put it in the crisper. Then I stashed three baseball bats in strategic places around the loft in case the situation got ugly. It was all I could think of.

I'd changed into dry clothes and put on sneakers. Another 'strategic' move, I thought to myself, the sneakers. The Oxy was working its magic, my nerves calmed and I was no longer sweating. But I was not high. I was simply not sick. My mind raced to figure the order of events in the last couple hours and how I could have avoided such a vulnerable position. The only conclusion I could draw, "you should've put the fuckin' chips in the safe you dumb motherfucker!"

Twenty five minutes passed since the text message. I stared out the window into the streets waiting to see Rhames coming. I felt foolish about the whole situation at the moment. Then came a knock on my door. I turned from the window and saw a silhouette on the other side of the smoked glass door. Too small to be Ving Rhames. I didn't move, then came another knock, on the glass part this time. The second round of knocking had an urgency about it. I went to the door. "Yeah, who is it?" I said, throwing bass into my voice.

"I got a delivery for PH205," a soft voice from the other side. A black female voice.

I unlocked the deadbolt, opened the door, and standing there in full United Postal Service uniform, rain gear and all, was a petite stern looking black woman. Her face was beautiful, strong and athletic. Package in one hand, mailbag over her shoulder, clipboard in the other. At a loss when she pushed past me, I closed the door as she walked over to the counter in the kitchen.

"Have you inspected the sample," she said as she used a short pocketknife to open the box.

"I did."

"Ok. This is how this is going to work. In this box is your order and you can count them and sample as you wish. But first you will hand over the money. I will go over there in your living room and count it. Next I will text my partner and let him know how much time I will be inside." She was a pro and this boosted my confidence.

"The money is in the fridge," I said and started toward it to open.

She held up her hand, signaling me to stay put. "That's fine. Here, take this," she said handing me the box containing ten small bottles with squared edges. I grabbed the box as she opened the fridge.

"It's in the bottom drawer, wrapped in tin foil. Twenty grand."

She took the foil brick and said, "Ok, like I said, I'm going to count it. How much time do you need?"

"Oh, uh, sorry," I stuttered, distracted by how beautiful she was. "Ten minutes is all I need."

"Cool."

I watched her walk to the sofa. She was typing a message into her phone. I couldn't make out her figure through the rain gear but she had a sexy walk. I put the box on the counter and twisted the top off of one of the bottles. It had a foil seal, cotton underneath, I removed both and poured the contents onto the counter, cupping my hand around the flow of pills. I counted in piles of ten. Five piles meant the quantity matched the label. I popped three into my mouth, began chewing them, reached into the fridge and grabbed a beer to wash them down. Then I grabbed another bottle of pills and repeated, sans the popping of more Oxycontin. She was eyeing me from the sofa as she peeled off bills into stacks of ten with her long fingers accentuated with long wildly colored fake nails. Her count was slow and tedious.

"Would you like something to drink," I asked her out of a habit for being polite to any type of company, especially of the female variety. The single pill that I'd taken almost a half hour ago seemed to be hitting me harder by the minute. I worried that three at one time was too much.

"I'm good," she said without slowing her count. Her eyes still trained on me as I put the counted pills back into the bottles.

The drugs were working at an accelerated rate. Euphoria was upon me. I grabbed another beer from the fridge and pounded half of it and jumped up to sit on the counter. Barely made it as my motor skills seemed to be lagging. "I like the rain gear. Incognito."

She flashed me a big smile showing off perfectly white teeth and paused the count, "incognito? Ha. So what's with this pimp ass penthouse loft you got here? Are you some kind of Hollywood player or just a drug dealer.....incognito?" She had a playful but sarcastic tone. I was turned on. She was so sexy and I felt idiotic for thinking and acting this way in this situation.

I couldn't resist though. "that's good. You sure you don't want a beer or something? A mixed drink perhaps. I only got beer, but there's a liquor store down the street?" She shook her head no and continued her count. Her essence grew more exotic by the second. My imagination began to run wild. "Alright, I see ya, you're all business. What about after work, you got plans?" I wasn't serious, just role-playing.

She shook her head as she counted the last of the cash then scooped up the stacks, placed them in a large manila envelope from her mailbag and sealed it with a lick of her tongue. "You really somethin' ain't ya?" She stood and walked toward me, placed her sexy hand on my thigh and said, "So, are we good?"

I felt a tingle in my crotch. "yeah we're good. It was nice doin' business with you people," I said as she flashed that brilliant smile one more time then walked to the door. "The offer for after work stands, you know where I live."

She said nothing and was gone. I locked the deadbolt behind her and laid down on the sofa and drifted off into an oxycodone haze with the TV playing a movie I was not watching. My world felt safe. Forgotten was the pain and torment of the last days. I did not think of anything as I laid there knowing I had enough medicine to keep me going for a long time. I was sure of it.

My phone vibrated from a text but it was on the kitchen counter, in another galaxy as far as I was concerned. I ignored it. I couldn't move from the serene cloud that was my sofa.

Twenty something hours and ten Oxy's later I checked my phone. The first message read, "TEXT INCOGNITO TO THIS NUMBER FOR THE FUTURE." The second through the fifth messages were from Timmy. Where have you been, hit me back, etcetera. I'd only thought of him a few times since that day at the pool. That seemed like a lifetime ago. I sent a reply telling him to stop by my place in a half hour. He hit me back right away, "YEAH BUDDY." I took a cold shower trying to straighten up and not be a zombie.

CHAPTER 21
GHOST

"Yo Mick, where the fuck have you been?", Timmy said when I opened the door.

"Come on in kid, grab a cold one," I said.

He grabbed two from the fridge, handed me one and made his way to the sofa. "you been shacked up with that fine assed bangtail from the pool this whole time, huh?"

I realized then that he had no idea about Leonora or her whereabouts. "nah man, just been busy, you know how that shit goes."

"You bullshittin' pal? I seen the SRT in the garage every day for weeks now, I knocked a couple times. Just figured you'd met your next wife," he said as he took a swig.

"Wish that was the case. Don't even know that chick's last name. Hell, I don't even have her phone number to tell you the truth." Took a long pull from the cold beer, "like to see her again though. You got her digits, kid?"

"You didn't even get her phone number," he looked at me with a dumbed down stare. "I thought you and her split that day, together. What was her name again? Lisa, right?"

"Leonora," saying the name made me sick to my stomach.

"Right, Leonora. I never got her number. Met her on the

sidewalk that day, being the salesman that I am, just threw out an invite to a pretty girl, she followed me to the roof and the rest is history."

"Yeah, the rest is history," I said staring out the window into sun and city haze. The rain was gone, but my life seemed to be an endless monsoon.

"Guy, it was all casual, those girls met each other that very same day, all strangers just minutes before you showed up. The luckiest pimp of all time, I was feelin' it, Mick. Especially when I saw you two off in your own world, making googly eyes at one another, fuckin' droolin' and whatnot. Where did you guys go anyway?"

I had to think of an answer. I changed the subject. "Look man, I think we're going to have to stick a pin in this project for awhile, some things came up that I gotta handle."

"Fuck man, what kind of shit? Already told you, whatever I can do to help out, I want to get the show on the road with this movie. There's people waiting on this thing. Man." He had a look of defeat.

My brain was foggy to say the least, I couldn't even remember the story line let alone come up with some sort of answer for my director. I offered the only remedy I could think of, "Listen kid, I'll throw you some more scratch to tide you over."

"You already know man, I don't borrow money."

"Consider it an advance, we'll work out the numbers down the road. How much do you need for rent, bills, whatever? Let me know and I'll give it to you. And like I said, it's not a loan so don't let it wear on you. Trust me, it would be a load off of my shoulders for the time being while I take care off this other shit."

"You're jammed up right now, huh?"

"A little bit. A little bit, kid. But it's nothin' I can't handle, just need a little time, maybe a month or so," the lies continued. I had no plan for anything. I felt like a real scumbag for lying, but all I could think of at the moment was calculating how long the pills were going to last and how much cash was left in the safe.

"What about these other cats that I lined up? I got us two cameramen that'll work for cash, a guy that has his own sound and lighting gear ready to go gorilla and work for cash, even says he's got a couple cousins that can do just about anything, and on the cheap. Man, I got the whole crew lined up. I used that money that you gave me, put some retainers down but that was a cool minute ago. We could lose that dough. I've already been shooting from the hip, makin' shit up so they don't bail on us," Timmy said sounding all grown up from his street hustling ways. I had admiration for him. I envied his focus. And his sobriety.   "We're gonna start comin' across as real fuckin' amateurs."

I laughed at the Lebowski quote. "Alright kid, I'll think of something, I'll give you some more cash to throw at the crew. What do you think? You feel out which one's are most critical to us, you know, indispensable. I want people that are hungry, like you."

"What if we started shooting this thing with me runnin' the show? I mean at least until you get your shit straightened out. I could start with the LA scenes. It's still your project, not tryin' to steal your thunder. You wrote the story, we got a working script. I'd feel a lot better about that than handing out money to people with only empty promises. Half of these people don't even believe you exist. Pretty soon your nick-name will be "The Ghost". Hey, that's a pretty good title, yeah "The Ghost"."

His idea sounded as good as any that I could think of. Suddenly my mind was working on his words. "That's not a bad idea Timmy. Not a bad idea at all. I don't know, let me think about it would ya?"

"Fuckin' A' my man. I'll be in my office this afternoon. Stop by and let me know, would ya Ghost?" He got up off the sofa and gave me a brotherly hug and a handshake. "And hey, whatever else I can do to help you with this other business, I'm all in buddy."

"I appreciate you, kid. I'll catch up with you in a bit, just gotta make a coupla calls," I said opening the door, Timmy entered the hallway. "And hey, if you got any of them girls' numbers ask them if they got any info on Leonora," I said in a casual manner.

"That broad really got you stuck huh? How is it you don't have her number?"

"Man, I forgot to save it on my phone," I said, which didn't make much sense. It showed on Timmy's face.

"I got one chick's number, I'll call her. My office awaits. In a minute brah."

"Yeah man, in a minute."

"Ghost," Timmy said to himself as he walked away.

CHAPTER 22
NAH BRO, PAT'S COOL

Timmy's proposal was sounding better by the minute as I thought with a clarity I hadn't experienced in weeks. After pacing around the loft for twenty minutes I said, "fuck it Mick, at this point what have you got to lose?" I did my best thinking when I spoke out loud to myself like a madman. Had no doubt that being full blown crazy was in the cards. Went into the safe, did a quick count, and grabbed a handful, threw it into my backpack and went out to my director's office poolside.

The glare of the sun permeated my sunglasses and its radiation on my skin felt therapeutic. The humidity smelled like summer even if it was snowing in other parts of the country. I found Timmy lounging by himself, half spent six-pack of tall boys within arms reach next to his lounge chair. He was the only sun worshipper by the pool that afternoon.

I reached down and grabbed a beer, and popped the top. Sleeping behind his shades, he came to with the crack of the beer. "Man, I thought I'd find you out here reworking the script, blue pen in mouth, red one in hand, marking the shit out of the pages that I'd written so long ago," I said with life in my gesture. I pulled up a chair and sat close.

He sprang up and pounded the beer from his lap that was

warm from his snooze, "no luck on those digits, buddy. That girl Melissa couldn't remember anything from that day. Fuckin' hippie chicks. This weed out here, man. Ten times as potent as the stuff from back in the day."

I cut short his diatribe, which I'd already heard a dozen times. "Listen, I thought about your idea. Fuck it, let's start shooting this thing," I said and handed him the stack of cash from the backpack. Sixty grand.

Timmy almost jumped out of the chair, "that's what I'm talkin' about mothafucka'."

"Get this thing started. I'll be checkin' in wit' you. I trust you, kid, so don't fuck this up. Any thing that you question, call me." The look on his face made me feel a whole lot better about the web of deceit that had become my life. At least now there was forward motion in the original plan.

I had a hundred grand remaining in the safe. The math behind this was simple. I didn't even want to game plan with him about the movie. Round numbers moved me, an inspired template for big ideas. Isn't that what we all sought out in life anyways? To be moved. It's what I sought out. I went for a drive.

Handing over that kind of money with such conviction had me riding a wave of confidence, opioid induced or not, it did not matter. I was focused, mojo in full effect as I cruised down the Santa Monica freeway. Decided I wouldn't waste too much time on this venture, but it was worth taking a shot in the dark. I drove to the building where Leonora lived and parked across the street from the gate that led to an open atrium with a pool. It was a two-story apartment building one would only see in southern California. At least it's where she lived before the crime of opportunity put her into a different tax bracket.

Sat there in my car hoping for some luck. Something to the

tune of her walking through that gate, spotting me, and crossing the street with a smile on her face. She'd say, "Mickey Fortunato, I knew you'd show up. Here's what you came for, right?" And then she'd hand over a bag of cash. Truth be told, I was clueless to how I would react to seeing her. Then something caught my eye. At the end of the block two police cruisers had come to an abrupt halt in the middle of the intersection with their cherries flashing. Within seconds four officers were rushing into another building similar to the one I was staking out.

Out of the corner of my eye someone was opening the gate to Leonora's building. It was her. Fuck. I froze for two seconds then jumped out of the car and crossed the street. The gate was locked but I eyed her climbing a flight of stairs leading to the second level. She proceeded down the walkway and went into an apartment. My heart was racing. I started pushing buttons on the directory panel. I avoided the button for the office. A voice came over the intercom, "Yeeess," said an elderly woman.

"I have a delivery for.." I scanned the names on the panel. "Mr. Schmidt."

"This is Ms. Robinson, but it's okay sweetie." She buzzed me in.

She held the buzzer down until I was already up the four steps to the atrium entrance.

The building was 1950's construction and the pool only contained about two feet of algae infused water in it. The plants were typical for these types of buildings, Bougainville everywhere, palm trees and a few cactus plants that had seen better days. Not one of the nicer buildings in Venice. When I reached the top of the stairs that Leonora had climbed I looked down and saw an elderly lady in a nightgown standing in her doorway looking around. Ms. Robinson I presumed. She looked up and saw me.

"Good afternoon Ms. Robinson," I said as if she was my neighbor. She smiled with a confused look on her face, gave a slight wave and went back into her apartment. I approached the door where Leonora had entered, #205, the blinds were closed on the window next to the door. I put my hand over the peephole and pressed my ear to the door. Heard a television with the volume turned up but no voices. I knocked. The volume on the TV went mute. No answer after ten seconds. I knocked once more, my heart racing.

The door opened, security chain engaged. Leonora's eyes appeared in the four-inch crack, "not a smart move Mickey," her voice not as sweet as the day we'd spent together.

"Not a smart move, huh," rage flooded my body and I smashed into the door with my shoulder, the force ripped the chain in half and the door slammed into her face. She flew backwards onto the floor as I charged in and kicked the door shut behind me. I pounced and straddled her this time, pinning her flailing arms to the floor. She was not a fighter and quickly submitted. "Where's my money, kid?"

"I don't know what you're talking about," she said in a calm voice, blood pouring from her nose. Then screamed, "Get the FUCK off of me! Pat!"

I thought for a second, Pat? Who the fuck?... from a blind spot to my right, a bare foot booted me squarely in the ribcage that sent me rolling off of Leonora. The pain shot through me and the wind left my chest cavity, long blond hair violently whipping across his face as he fed me trained punches, one after another, only one landing with accuracy, a shot to my jaw. The ambush happened so fast and furious for a second I thought it was Leonora pummeling me. I managed to roll away and get to my feet. He charged me with a haymaker, I ducked it and slipped behind him with a chokehold. He had at least four inches and forty pounds on me with a neck and arms too muscular for me to slip a full nelson and get him to the ground. I began to press a thumb with everything I had into his eye socket, while my other arm squeezed with every ounce of strength to control him by his neck. It was an awkward position for both of us. Then something struck my shoulder blade with such force I let the longhaired assailant free from my grip and fell straight to the floor. The pain was instant and dull with agony. Left me useless.

Looking up, my senses fading to black, Leonora was midswing when the man snatched the baseball bat from her grip using one hand as if she were a small child. He used his other hand to push her away. Her face was bloodied and looked as if she was screaming. I heard nothing as I lost consciousness.

When I came to, they were standing over me. This guy looked like the wrestler Triple H, a muscled giant with bronze skin. He held the bat in one hand, she was breathing heavy with a bloody wad of paper towels pressed to her nose. "Where's my fuckin' money?" I muttered with a twinge of rage. I tried to raise my hand from the carpet but a lightning bolt of pain shot through my body and made me stifle a yelp. Busted ribs at the very least.

"You just stay down there bro, if you know what's good for ya," Triple H said.

"You motherfucker," Leonora sounded as if she wanted this guy to kill me.

"I'm the motherfucker. Yo Pat, is this your girlfriend here?" I said, the words coming between short painful breaths.

"That's right, she's my girlfriend. Who are you?" He had an innocent way about him, obviously not the brightest bulb in the closet.

"She didn't tell you about me Pat?" I confused him with the question. "Tell him, kid."

He looked to her, "tell me what Leonora," still in a dumb and innocent tone. The gentle giant with steel fists and Ray Guy's foot.

"He's just some guy I met awhile back," she said with the same look as him on her no longer flawless face. "So what, are you stalking me or something? How did you know where I lived you fucking creep," she said then tried to kick my feet but whiffed and hit the leg of the turned over coffee table, "aaaaahh-hhh, MOTHERFUCKER!"

I laughed at the gaff. Triple H grabbed her shoulder as she loaded up for another attempt, then said, "so...where and when did you two meet?" As confused as a Mormon walking into a Tijuana donkey show, his eyes not knowing who to look at.

"Listen, Pat, or should I call you Patrick, after all you just thoroughly kicked my ass and held your lovely girlfriend off of me, which I find mighty gentlemanly of you by the way."

"Nah bro, Pat's cool," he said.

I felt a connection with this guy. Leonora was exposed as a schemer. "Hey Pat, you mind if I sit up, the room is spinning."

"Yeah bro," he said and reached out one of his frying pan sized hands and helped me up. I made it to the sofa, the pain made me see black and purple spots.

"AAhhh, thanks Pat," I groaned trying to find a seated position that didn't hurt. No such luck. Leonora let out a gasp and stormed out of the room. "I didn't expect you to be living in such squalor since your big payday in Vegas," I said as loud as I could through a wince.

"What's that supposta mean?" Mr. WrestleMania asked.

"It means that you guys should be beating up intruders in digs a little bit more posh than this." Still the look of confusion from Pat. "Your girl came up on almost a half million dollars not too long ago and that is why, my oversized surfer friend, I am sitting on your sofa with a bunch of broken ribs."

"He's full of shit Pat. Like I said he's a fuckin' stalker, don't listen to this shit baby," Leonora said as she sidled up next to him with balls of toilet paper stuffed into her once perfect nostrils. It was a ridiculous sight to see. The unsympathetic look on Pat's face almost made me feel vindicated.

"You got a half mill and I'm bustin' my ass doing' stunts on B-movies for scale?" He turned his full attention to his girl. "At least we could get a new car, like a Hummer or something," Pat continued, backing Leonora into the kitchen and out of view from where I sat.

I saw my opening. I rushed toward the door and into the sunlight. Adrenaline got me to my car. Oxycodone would make the rest of my day possible.

I planned to hit the 405, head south to look for my next bank in Orange County. By the time I made the intersection of Venice Boulevard and Sawtelle the pain was getting to me. Scratched that plan and continued east on Venice all the way back to downtown.

On the drive I came to grips with the fact that I'd gotten pretty lucky back in Venice, alive to fight another day. I could've made a call or two, hired some muscle from back home to help me retrieve the money. But I decided to stick to my guns. Work alone. That money was destined for another story. Fuckin Leonora from Venice...and Pat!

Knew I had it in me to knock off another three or four banks. But first I'd need the friendly confines of my loft, up the dose on my meds, numb the actual physical pain, lick my wounds for a day or two. Steel myself then get back to the hunt.

When I took my shirt off in the bathroom mirror, the sight confirmed what I already knew. The right side of my midsection was already dark purple with red blotches. Probably had three or four cracked ribs. I was getting used to the rhythm of short shallow breaths. The bruising was almost identical to what I'd seen on my body when I fell fifteen feet onto a pile of cast-iron water pipes ten years back. I was out of work for almost four months then. Didn't have to climb around on the iron now, I just needed to hop over a couple of bank counters. Still a daunting task with that type of the pain. Had to keep up my heavy drug regimen, simple as that.

———————

Drifting in and out of a restless sleep for the next ten hours, it was a torturous convalescence. The Oxy's didn't seem to do much for the sharp pains felt whenever I rolled over. At three in the morning my phone started ringing. Reaching for it I screamed in pain, dropped it under the coffee table, and screamed some more as I struggled to figure out the least painful way to reach it. It was Liana.

"Mickey."

CHAPTER 23
ROOM WITH AN OCEAN VIEW

t took me ten minutes to drive from Sixth and Main to Providence St. John's in Santa Monica. Once I was in the hospital, it took me twice as long to finally see her face. Suddenly nothing else in the world mattered. I couldn't feel the broken bones in my chest cavity. I was racked with guilt and self-loathing, a depression of a desperate magnitude set in at the sight of seeing her through the safety glass window.

Liana found her unconscious on the living room floor the day before. She went into cardiac arrest as they were putting her in the ambulance. Jackie was actually gone for at least a minute until they resuscitated her on the way to the hospital. She'd overdosed on a heroin and Xanax combination. Liana wasn't even going to call me until she made the short trip back to her place to shower. She said she scrolled Jackie's phone and couldn't bring herself to call anyone. "But I found this in her book bag." Liana handed me an envelope. "Mickey My Love," it read on the envelope.

I felt like a coward for not being able to open the letter let alone read it. I put it in my pocket, but reached for it a thousand times, never working up the courage to read.

I stayed in the waiting room of the hospital for the better part of the next two days, returning to my loft once to shower and grab more meds. Every pill that I chewed felt like razorblades going down knowing what Jackie had just gone through. They had a psych hold on her. I wasn't the husband or family and was not allowed to see her. I was in no shape to fight bureaucracy or confront authority. So I waited.

A nurse stopped by the waiting area a few times to give me updates if there were any to give.

"I don't know the status of you and your girlfriend's relationship but I'm going to weigh in on something. That girl is going to be fine. Contingent on two things. First, she desperately needs to go to some sort of rehabilitation facility. Then she's gonna need some help, she's young, she needs her family. I've talked with her and she's ashamed to let them know what her life has become so far away from home. She says that you will take care of her, pay for rehab. But I'll be honest with you Mr. Fortunato, from the looks of you, I'd say that you are the last person this girl needs in her life. She told me you don't even use drugs. That tells me a lot," she spoke without malice but I could see the motherly look of disdain.

I was searching for words and about to speak but she continued.

"Do the right thing for this girl. She must be what, ten years younger than you? She's got her whole life ahead of her. You appear to have your own problems. It's my not so bold prediction that we'll be seeing you right back here in the future."

"I appreciate your honesty but you don't know anything about me, lady," the contemptuous words from my mouth made me sick with myself. Everything this nurse was saying was true.

"It's easy to see it in your face, you're an addict just like your girlfriend in there. And the fact that she lied to me about you only leads me to believe that you and her are headed toward early graves. If that's some kind of sick and twisted romantic vision the two of you share, I can arrange a tour of the morgue, we got three opioid od's down there right now."

She disappeared down the hallway. Five minutes later she reappeared, pushing Jackie in a wheelchair. The sight broke my soul. I fought back tears. Jackie's own tears were flowing silently down her pale cheeks to her chapped lips. She looked like a child in that chair, much too young to be my girlfriend.

"You want to grab a bite," I said, breaking the silence after driving for five minutes. We were already a couple blocks from Liana's house.

"I'm not hungry," she said as she stared out the passenger window, blowing cigarette smoke into the California winter sunshine. "Where are we going?"

"I hadn't really thought about it. I just figured you'd want to go back to Liana's."

"I don't want to go back there."

"Ok," followed by another silence. I started to head north to catch the Pacific Coast Highway at California Ave. "Let's just drive for awhile. Whattya say, kid?"

"Sure," she said, a lump forming in her throat. "Fuck, Mickey, I'm so fucked up right now," tears were in heavy flow, nose was already a river as she covered her face with her hands.

I reached my hand over and began to massage the nape of her neck. Her body quaked as she attempted to stifle the violent sobs. "Come on Jackie baby, we're gonna be alright, kid. Gonna to make sure of it."

We drove to Malibu without saying another word to each other. We got coffee at Starbucks and sat on the side of the road, leaning against my car, staring off into the setting sun.

"Liana found the letter," I said as I placed my arm around her.

"I know Mickey, she told me. I meant every word. But what the fuck am I supposed to do now, I feel like such a fool." She lowered her head in shame, staring at her feet while she put her arm around me.

"I'm gonna take you to this rehab place just up the road from here. We'll go there when you're ready, but it's gotta be today. I called over there yesterday, talked to the director, told him the situation and he said the best thing we could do was get you there as soon as they released you from the hospital. Whattya say Jackie?"

"I don't know Mickey, I feel pretty fuckin' low. I just want to spend some time with you.."

I tightened my embrace and said, "Listen baby, I know you're low, I'm right there in that place with you. But this is the best thing we can do right now. I checked this place out, looks beautiful. You'll have a room with an ocean view."

She sighed as she swung around to hug me proper, burying her face in my chest and squeezing with all her sapped strength. "I want to go back to better days. God, I wish this was all just a dream and I'd wake up with your warm hands on me."

I reached both of my hands under her t-shirt and started rubbing her back the way she liked it. "We'll get back to those days, kid. One thing at a time baby."

I took Jackie to rehab and drove back to my loft to eat pills. Malibu cost me seventy grand. I paid the director in cash, no questions asked, no paperwork. I was wondering if it would go straight into his pocket when I left his office. I didn't care, as long as Jackie would be safe. I felt awful for leaving her there. I knew it was for the best but I really wanted to lay next to her warm body, I wanted to confess everything. I wanted to lock the door behind us and vanish into the dream world we shared before.

CHAPTER 24
THE THROW AWAY

Sleep was almost nonexistent on the steady diet of Oxys. I'd been poppin' three or four at a time every few hours and the itching that came with this pill made me forget about the busted ribs. But the drugs were doing me no favors in mentally preparing myself to go back into a bank. I was struggling for confidence.

That next morning I counted my bankroll. I had less than thirty grand left. That was all the motivation I needed. I placed the money back in the safe and laughed. I had only a little more now than when I'd hit the bank in San Dimas. I needed more money.

I made my way down to Orange County to scout out my next job. As I drove south on the 5 I thought about how cruel and unforgiving the world seemed to me. Gone was the sense that I was trying to do something noble with the odds stacked against me.. Replacing that delusion was a sense that I was rushing headlong into the abyss when I thought of the endgame. I'd needed to get at least another three or four hundred grand. That would mean another ten, twelve banks. The Oxy's would be gone in another couple weeks. I'd have to figure out what to do with Jackie sooner than I knew it. I'd have to give Timmy more money soon. I felt so overwhelmed that thoughts of suicide began to creep to the fore of my conscience. It was almost impossible to envision a future without these drugs. Getting out of this dark hole seemed a more daunting task. My biggest fear though was getting caught. The prospect of going to prison was a constant thought. Prison in and of itself is not what I feared most. I feared being a bust out in life. I could hear my father's voice, 'You only get one crack at this lifetime Mickey, make the most of it.'

I hated myself for the choices I'd made, but all of that faded when I exited the 5 near Laguna Hills, south of Santa Ana. The adrenaline woke me from self-pity. The area looked promising. I popped a few pills, chewed them to dust and washed it down with a Rockstar. It felt good to be so far from the city that had started feeling like Alcatraz in the last few weeks. The Pixies 'Where is My Mind' happened to play on the radio, then I spotted it, my next job.

The bank stood alone on a corner, set back from the four lane boulevard about a hundred feet from the street's edge. Windows not tinted, I could see inside the bank from a shopping mall parking lot across the way. I called Gato.

"Yooooo, what's up doggy? I been thinkin' you made the big time, like you were forgetting about us little vatos. So what's up fool?" His voice full of energy.

Focus came instantly as I stared into the bank's windows, feeling outlaw once again, triggered by the phone call. "Gato, you know I never forget my homies. How you been, my guy?"

"I can't call it doggy, you know, livin' the dream. Man, my girl's got another lil' vato on the way so I'm glad you called," his voice leaned serious at the tail end.

"You got another kid on the way? Shit man, you ain't doin' nothin for your people's stereotypes, ese," I said and we laughed for a second. "Well, check it out then. I want to see your guy again, I'll throw a little extra your way this time, for diapers and tamales."

"Yeah fool, I'll call him. When you wanna get up wit' him?"

"I was thinking tomorrow, can you make it happen?"

"I'll hit him up right now, get wit you in a minute, fool."

"Sounds good, kid," I said.

"Hey Mickey?"

"Yeah man, what's up?"

"You gonna come by the crib and kick it any time soon? I want to take you for a ride in the Lincoln, got that motha roarin', fool," he said sounding a little off.

"For sure. Something else on your mind Gato?"

"Man, dog...I didn't want to even tell you but.."

"Gato, it's cool, man. I knew you'd sell that thing sooner or later," I said, relieved in a way.

"I know what that car meant, just..."

"Hey, kid, don't think twice about it. But if it's a boy, do me a solid."

"Yeah man, of course you'll be his Padrino!"

"Since you asked, yeah I'll be the little homie's godfather. But I was gonna say you gotta name him Monte."

Laughing on the other end, "don't know if the mamacita's gonna go for that one but I'll think about it dog."

"Bustin your balls Gato. Hit me back when you talk to your guy."

The bank was another Chase, four blocks from the expressway, no stop signs or lights. From my vantage point it looked like there were three teller stations, no security guard and no drive through. I took a short ride around the mall to see the layout. Most of the cars seemed to be parked on the opposite side of the mall from where the bank was at. I exited the sprawling lot and drove past the bank and into the residential area off of the main boulevard.

Palm trees lined winding streets leading to a hilly area where the houses grew in size the further from the boulevard I roamed. This would be no place to go if the heat drew down on me. My phone rang as I was turning around in an empty cul-de-sac of McMansions still under construction.

"Talk to me kid," I said hoping for good news.

"You good to go, homie. Text me the time and place and he'll be there tomorrow."

"What you got goin' on in a few hours, Gato?"

"Shit. You thinkin' about swingin' through the hood?"

"Yeah, fuck it. I'll bring the beers."

"Bet. Alright dog, later then."

I pulled up along side the bank and saw two tellers through the windows, both female, and said out loud, "I'll see you tomorrow, ladies."

Headed back toward the expressway and decided I'd park the G-ride in the mall parking lot where I was earlier. Though I'd have to run across the road and it would be easy to get a make on the vehicle for anyone looking out the bank windows, I would have quick access to the expressway. I clocked the route. Forty five seconds and I was heading up the circular ramp to head back north toward LA. A mile down the highway was an exit for Lake Forest Drive. I exited and the plan came into focus. Your typical suburban wasteland, fast food places and strip malls in each direction. Perfect spot to swap out the G-ride. Another jolt of adrenaline sent my spirits soaring, the first time in a while I felt a sense of joy. It was strange, but the thought of action made me feel productive and all of the shit that I'd gotten myself involved with could be overcome. If I could pull this whole thing off, I thought. Hit a few more banks, make this movie, hell, maybe even take myself to Malibu once the film was in the can...I knew I was getting ahead of myself but it didn't matter. I knew that I was haphazard in my planning, that didn't seem important any more. I knew that I'd already crossed a certain threshold in my life and that from here on out it would all be a gamble. Couldn't hate the world for what I'd become like so many desperadoes often did. If this story could be told years down the road, I would do my part in supplying the action. And hopefully be the hero.

Gato was on the street in front of the tiny house finishing a wax job on his father's behemoth car. His face lit up when he saw me park behind the 1979 Lincoln Mark V on 47th street, but he kept with his waxy circles. Not wearing his usual rags, the khaki's were crisp and creased, boots shiny, his dago-t was still bright white and tight. His hair was slicked to a vinyl sheen. "Wow, fuckin' clean! Those the side-pipes from the Monte?" I said as I stepped from the SRT8.

He set the can of Meguiar's Carnauba and the rags on the curb, took a step back and gave the gigantic car a look of admiration, smiled, gave me a wink and said, "you know it fool! I took em off before I sold it."

"Nice. You come up a little bit at least?"

His smile faded, "come on doggie, don't hit a vato when he's down."

"Fuckin' with you ese, I hope you got double what you paid for it…you keep popping out a kid every nine months."

"Mr. Hollywood always wit the jokes. Tell you what, give you a shot at the title," he nodded at the SRT then at the Mark V. "We can go to the river, race for pink slips, doggy? What you think, Grease Lightning?"

I tried to give him dead eyes but neither of us could hold it long. We started laughing and moved in for a handshake and a hug, I winced a little when I raised my arms. "I fuckin' missed you, kid," I said. I meant it too. Gato was the only friend that I had on the west coast that always made me feel at home.

He looked at me, then at the Lincoln and said, "come on Mickey, let's take it for a ride. I gotta show you what this bad boy can do."

"Fuckin' A', let's go. Gotta hit a liquor store anyways." I just wanted to give him some cash and discuss business matters but Gato's mojo was contagious.

We hopped in the Lincoln. He turned the key and the thing growled. He looked at me with a feral smile a mile wide, lowered his Locs and we took off on a crawl, hung a right on Central Avenue and hit the gas. The front end lifted and the side-pipes roared, drowning out our laughs. We cruised slow for a block, he wanted to be seen in the shiny boat. We passed a couple of packs of cohorts on different corners, Gato bobbing his head, getting whistles and smiles in return. He was in his glory. We continued straight, making every light for a mile.

"So what's up with you Mickey? I'll speak the truth, dog. You don't look right," he said and twisted his still tilted back head to me as he drove slow. The question punched me in the kidney.

"Man, just been havin' a rough go of it lately, kid."

"What's up with this, doggy?" He said pointing at the side of my torso.

The compression wrap that I'd been wearing was visible through my t-shirt, "it's nothing, just a couple bruised ribs. Listen Gato, I got some cash for you, but I got a special request." It was difficult for me to ask a friend to put himself out there.

"Come out wit' it Big Time."

"I need a piece, a throw-away."

He looked over at me for a second then hit the gas pretty hard and the Lincoln let out a guttural purr. "I got you *carnal*," he said speaking loud and proud, his head tilted back, "what type of burner you want?"

Everything was on impulse at that point. It wasn't even a

conscious decision to ask for a gun, it simply came out of the outlaw's mouth. "Nothin' heavy. It's not to shoot, at least I hope not."

"Listen doggy," he slowed the Lincoln down, "if you're gonna be packin' heat, for whatever dog, that piece ought to be able to bring it, know what I'm sayin'?"

He was right. I'd never even shot a gun, only held one a few times at that. Strange getting advice from Gato. I'd always felt like an older brother to him, but I quickly realized that I was in foreign territory now. "Can you get somethin' for me by tomorrow morning?"

He didn't even look at me as he took a sharp right heading west on Washington Boulevard. We continued over the bridge spanning the LA River, which was flowing from the recent rain. Past the bridge we hooked a right down a hilly gravel road and pulled into the gated lot of a small junkyard surrounded by a raggedy sheet metal fence topped with concertina razor wire. A Rottweiler was chained up near the open garage door where a forklift sat. Both the dog and the machine seemed to be of little use any more. The Rott barely raised an eye, Gato killed the engine. "you got cash on you?"

I handed him two grand in hundred dollar bills. "I was gonna give you five bills for the g-ride. This is a separate favor, so make a deal and keep the change. Cool?"

"I'll be back in a minute, homie." He exited the car and disappeared into the garage.

Two minutes later he emerged from the side of the building, walking slowly, accompanied by another man. Gato had a small paper bag in his hand. The other guy was a large Mexican, late forties, early fifties, black hair with white streaks pulled back into a ponytail. His get-up identical to Gato, arms covered in jailhouse tats, full push broom mustache and a number thirteen tattooed in place of a goatee. Gato signaled me with a hand wave.

As soon as I got out of the Lincoln the Rott sprang to action as if it had been stuck with a cattle prod, lunging in my direction, slobber flying violently with his big-dog sized barks. The heavy chain barely restrained him. The Mexicans started laughing.

"Chua!" the big man barked. The dog returned to catatonic in an instant. "The old boy still got it homes," he said to a laughing Gato. "Your old man will be proud, ese," he said as they walked toward me, admiring the Lincoln.

"Mickey this is the homie Spider," Gato said, really pouring on the East LA tilt in his voice as he walked to the driver's side, opened the door and put the paper bag under the seat.

Spider reached his hand out and I shook it. A gentle shake from a hand hard as concrete, almost twice as big as mine. "Spider, a pleasure," I said, giving a smile to Gato that said, 'wow, this is one big motherfucker'. His massive frame would've made my friend Pat in Venice look like an average Joe.

"Spider goes back wit my pops since when they were little vatos in East Los," Gato said with pride written on his face.

"Where you from homes?" Spider asked me.

"Chicago, but I stay in LA these days."

Spider just nodded his head and returned his stare to the Lincoln. "I knew those pipes would look good on this beast."

Gato's demeanor got serious, "this fool right here inspired me, they came off his Pops' ride."

Spider turned his attention to me, "that right. What year was that Monte?"

A pang of guilt hit me, "1970. My brother fixed it up for me a couple years back. Pipes from a Corvette Stingray."

Spider held out his massive right forearm and pointed to an old, blurred tattoo. It was a large crucifix with the date 4/14/70 inscribed at the cross section and three names, 'Green Eyez, Drowsy, and Solo', one name next to each of the upper three points. "My *carnalitos* didn't make it up state with us. We were just a bunch of crazy fools, actin hard. 1970."

"Fuckin' heavy, Spider," was all I could say. My mind was drifting back to the past.

Spider stared at me, stroking his push broom, "homie says you're making a movie?"

"Spider, this fool here can tell great stories, this white boy is gonna be famous one day, no question."

The adulation made me feel like a fraud knowing that I just came here to get a gun to rob banks. "Yeah, we'll see, might end up infamous the way this movie is going right now," I said wishing I was only half joking.

"Hey Spider, we gotta bounce," Gato said as they shook and gave each other a big hug.

"Mickey, it was good to meet you. Good luck with your movie, come through some time, we'll throw back a couple of cervezas and swap stories."

"All right man."

We hopped in the car, Gato fired it up and gave it some gas a few times. Spider was all smiles and waved to us while Gato peeled out of the lot. Half way across the bridge he handed me the paper bag from under his seat. I didn't look inside, but I felt the weight when I placed it under my seat. "I really appreciate you, Gato."

He held out the wad of hundreds I gave him, "here dog, take it."

"Nah, man, it's yours kid."

"Serio, take the money, Mick." He never called me 'Mick', it was always dog or doggie, homes or homie, and Mickey when he was feeling good. He had a serious look on his face, "I told Spider that it was for one of the homies, cost me nothing. Serio, take the money, Mick, I know you got some shit goin' down. Plus, I did come up little bit on the Monte, so…"

He was still holding it out, I pushed it back towards him, "you can buy the cervezas. Cool?"

We hit a liquor store on Central a couple blocks from his

house and drank a couple in his garage. I wrote down the location for his boy to meet me with the G-ride in the morning.

He walked me out to the SRT8 and said to me under the streetlight, "you take care Mick. Wish you would take the dough, but hey, if you say you straight...then you straight."

"Good lookin' out, Gato. I'll catch you on the flip side."

CHAPTER 25
PHIL THE COWARD AND THE O.C. FOLLIES

leep was becoming a fond and distant memory. I laid on the sofa all night trying to be lulled into distraction with the TV on. Instead, I spent hours feeling the weight and possibility of the .357 Magnum. Countless scenarios played out in my mind while I debated whether or not to purchase ammunition for this new tool that came without a defined purpose. I wondered if bullets would swing the door wide open, extending a warm and welcome invitation to the reaper himself. Beginning to think schizophrenia came in my welcoming basket to this world.

I arrived two hours early at the spot to meet Spantos. A parking lot of a Ramada Inn near the 5 in Lake Forest, just a couple of miles from the bank. Nerves were on alert but under control. I was hoping that there would be more cars parked in the lot, there were only ten or twelve. It would have to do. The thought of turning back was a forgone conclusion. I knew that getting busted robbing a bank with a gun, loaded or not, would fetch me some serious time, possibly life. It felt good to have sight of an ultimate outcome. Diminishing the number of possibilities gave a feeling of relief. The .357 brought an eerie sense of control to my thoughts.

Spantos and his partner showed up on time. Tweakers or not, they were punctual. I always respected this quality in people, and it was a long drive from the city. The same F150 as before tailed a late model Mercedes sedan, silver. It wasn't flashy but it was nicer than I'd expected, it had tinted windows with stock rims. No front plate, it would be perfect, I thought.

Both cars parked in the hotel parking lot. I wasn't sure that they saw me parked on the street about two hundred feet away as I had some cover with a big elm tree. Still wearing my street clothes, I got out and walked over to where Spantos was getting out of the Mercedes. He was about to hop into the pickup when I yelled out, "Spantos."

I handed him the cash, he handed me an actual key this time. "Good doin' business with you again."

"Check it out dog, call me when you are finished with this ride, I'm gonna flip it and chop it. Let me know where it is and I'll have the homie pick it up."

Didn't want to have a personal connection to this guy and his 'homie' but he was Gato's boy, "you can come back here this afternoon, I'll leave the key in the rear passenger wheel well," I said with trepidation, thinking how this could come back to burn me, the getaway vehicle from a bank robbery right down the road being parked here all afternoon.

"I appreciate it, fool. The next one is on the house, my boy."

I walked back to my car and watched them leave before putting on my work uniform. Already wearing slacks, I added a white dress shirt, suit jacket and tie. A dark curly wig with a Magnum P.I. mustache, a pair of large rose tinted framed glasses and I looked ridiculous. But unrecognizable. I popped five Oxy's, grabbed the hours-cold coffee from the console, stuffed the moneybag into my jacket's inside pocket and strode to the Mercedes. The pistol was heavy in the right pocket of the suit coat. With every lapse in planning, I felt a burning sensation in the pit of my stomach. Voices in my head would shout, 'What the fuck is wrong with you, be fuckin' smart.' I wanted to hear my father's voice but the guilt wouldn't allow it.

I sat and waited a few minutes while two customers who were finishing their business at the teller counter exited the front door. The .357 would have to wait to make its debut. I left it under the seat in the G-ride and crossed the street to the bank. It was show time.

Upon entering, my blood went cool, I felt at home, a sound-track played in my head. I did not know who sang the song or the title, a 70's funk track, a tasty lick from Jackie's mix. I approached the counter where there was only one teller, a plain looking blonde in her late twenties. Everything about her was average, height, weight, looks, a real plain Jane. Behind her and to the left about twenty feet was another woman, long dark hair, ankle length navy skirt and cheap pumps. She looked like a librarian.

"How can we help you today, sir," Plain Jane said with apprehension behind her smile. Up close the disguise was ill fitting and the garish glasses were over the top.

I gleaned the nametag, "you can start by putting your hands on the counter so I can see them, Amber. Listen to what I'm saying and I will be out of here in less than a minute, sweet-heart. This is a hold up, so just be cool. Now, I want you to keep your eyes on me. Do not think of anything besides my words; no silent alarms, no tracers, no dye packs. Do you understand me, Amber?" Almost called her Jane.

She nodded slowly. The smile she wore moments ago was now a grimace, as if she was constipated. Her cheeks were flushed, her eyes wide and on the verge of twitching.

"Now I want you to open the drawer and take from it only

the large bills, twenties, fifties and hundreds and place them on the counter." As she was doing this the librarian turned and started to walk over. She stopped about five feet behind Amber and cocked her head slightly as she looked at me. I remained focused. "Now remove the straps on those twenties and hundreds." Hearing these instructions, the librarian turned away and moved back toward the filing cabinet. I jumped the counter and landed awkwardly on the other side. It knocked the wind out of me and the pain in my ribcage overthrew the opioid relief. Amber stepped away from the counter and laid down face first on the floor next to where I was getting to my feet. She held her hands out in front of her as if I'd shouted these instructions.

"Hey honey, stay right where you are," I said to the librarian who froze instantly. I was in serious pain trying to speak. "Where's the money drawer or day safe?" Way off script and rage was on the horizon, I was about to lose my cool.

"I..I don't know what you are talking about sir," she said in a quivering voice.

"I'm not asking. Show me to the cash you use to fill the teller drawers. Now!"

"Sir, it's in the back room."

The back room, I thought to myself, fuck, I should've brought the pistol. I grabbed her by the arm and shouted, "which way, sweetheart?"

She pointed past me and I spun her around only to see a man standing in a doorway fifteen feet in front of us. He raised his hands over his head. Guess I didn't even need the gun.

"He wants the safe, Phil," said librarian.

"You have the key," Phil replied back.

"Get on the fuckin' floor Phil, just like Amber over there," I growled and he complied in militant fashion. "Give me the key," I said in librarian's ear. She went to raise the arm I was holding tightly and pointed with her free hand to her other wrist. I grabbed the key ring that was attached to a fluorescent pink-coiled bracelet, the kind a schoolgirl would wear as jewelry, and stripped her of it. "Take me to the safe, and don't try to be a hero, Phil."

The librarian and I stepped over Phil sprawled out on the floor and came to the room. I let go of her arm and handed her the pink coil, "open it." She was cool with the key. We entered and she crossed the room and knelt in front of a small safe that was tucked up underneath a counter top. I was right behind her, and when it was open I grabbed her arm and knelt beside her, pulled out the moneybag and began filling it. She was shaking, I said, "relax, I'm almost out of your hair."

"The police will be here any minute you know." Her words made my heart stop.

I zipped up the bag which was full, grabbed the last couple bundles of cash, stuffed them into pockets and bolted out of the room to the teller area and scanned the windows. No police yet. On the way back over the counter I saw a man coming through the front door. My adrenaline redlined, pain was not a factor this time around, I stuck the landing. Instincts took over and I ran the poor guy over like Bo Jackson did to The Boz at the goal line. He somersaulted backwards, his head slammed into the door he'd just walked through and sent it flying back open. Without breaking stride I hurdled The Boz and exploded through the sally port to daylight. Eyes wildly scanning the street for oncoming traffic and sirens……..nothing. A mad dash over the pavement and I was back in the Mercedes, its engine still running, and within seconds was on my way to the expressway.

A full city block from the 5 overpass, two cruisers with their sirens ablaze were heading toward me at a furious clip. Glanced into the rearview and saw another set of cherries pulling into the bank's parking lot. I ripped the wig and mustache off in a single motion and swerved into oncoming traffic for a split second, approaching cruisers were in the far right hand lane as I passed them. Eyes trained on the rearview, I saw brake lights and smoke as the trailing squad car fishtailed into a U-turn. Buried the gas pedal and the finely tuned piece of German machinery took off like a bullet train. I cut a hard left and veered onto the northbound ramp by the time the cruiser made the U-turn and rebounded, headed my way. The Mercedes handled like a champ up the ramp. By the time I had it straightened out and merged into traffic, I was doing eighty. Cars were disappearing in my wake as I approached a hundred and fifty. In the volatile maneuvering I didn't have a clear line of sight or time enough to see how far the police trailed. Within a minute I hit the exit to where the SRT8 was parked.

I descended down the ramp, the thought of blowing through the light at the bottom and running for safety in the Mercedes crossed my mind. I looked at the fuel gauge. It was an eighth of a tank, "fuckin' drug addict, dumb fuckin' asshole!!" I screamed aloud for the only dumb fuckin' drug addicted asshole to hear.

I made a right at the bottom of the ramp, then another quick right. I was going the wrong way down a one-way street and the car heading toward me knew it. It swerved, I swerved slightly to my right, his horn blowing as I flew by him at ninety miles an hour. Passing the hotel on my left I continued to the end of the parking lot, cut the wheel and jumped the curb to avoid an eighteen wheeler headed for me. The Mercedes bucked wildly and I heard the rims bang with a thud as I hit the curb. I cleared the grassy embankment at the edge of the lot and made the German disc brakes earn their money. Jumped into the SRT and took off.

I slammed on the brakes as the follies of a drug addicted criminal continued. I forgot the .357 in the Mercedes.

Threw the SRT8 into gear and reversed all the way into a back-end fishtailed stop next to the g-ride. There it sat, still running, driver's side door still open. I grabbed the pistol, which was now near the brake pedal, and took off, pounding the steering wheel in fury. With the wheels falling off of my sloppily planned day I was expecting heat on the scene on the 5. Instead, there was nothing but civilian traffic for the first two miles. It wasn't a roadblock but there were two unmarked cruisers and two California Highway Patrol cars on the right shoulder just before the Laguna Freeway junction. Probably waiting for a bulletin over the radio, whether or not it was for the bank I had no idea. But I had to play the game as if I was made. Once I was a good half-mile past the cop convention I hit the gas hard... Hard...had to put some immediate distance between me and the scene. At a hundred and forty I was traveling more than two miles a minute. I made it to Commerce in fifteen minutes. Slowed down and exited at Washington, pulled over and threw up. Half of it on my door, half of it on the pavement, a mix of coffee, pills and blood. Dry heaves followed and the pain emanating from my chest cavity was almost intolerable. It took ten minutes before I could catch my breath, and the second I closed the car door my phone began vibrating, "yeah, what's up kid," I answered like I'd just finished a set of a hundred pushups.

"The fuck, my man. What? You just get finished fuckin' that fat chick from 747," Timmy said referring to the fat chick that lived on the seventh floor.

I let out a laugh that almost brought back the heaves. "Don't guy."

"Don't what? Remind you of the 747 jumbo jet that lives in 747? The chick that's so big she rides the service elevator to her floor? Or you don't want me to remind you that, yeah, I fucked her," he continued, sensing that I didn't want to laugh at the moment but wanting to make me any way.

"Guy, I'm serious," I said, gasping for air, laughing and wincing like a mad man, the stench of vomit and lunacy pungent in the car as I headed west on Washington.

"Guy... I'm serious too, had to roll her around in flour just to find the wet spot and when I finished she thanked me for bangin' one of her fat rolls."

I hung up and kept laughing, the pain made me want to pullover and puke again. He called right back.

"Timmy, I'm serious, kid. What's goin' on?"

"Alright, alright, I just called to tell you that I'm shooting a couple of scene's tonight and I wanted to see if you wanted to swing through. Camera will start rolling at ten o'clock. Gonna start at MacArthur Park, then I got three rooms over at the Olympic Hotel, 7th and Westlake."

I was trying to think of the scenes he was going to shoot when it dawned on me. "Guy, you're gonna shoot the ending already," I said remembering the part of the story that could take place in MacArthur Park.

"Makes sense on paper. I was gonna film a few interior scenes at the Olympic, you know, see how it shows up on the camera. At the very least I get some gritty old-school B-roll."

"The Olympic? What kind of hotel are we talkin, kid?"

"It's a real shit hole. Hookers, junkies, real down on their luck kind of motherfuckers. They got afternoon specials and weekly rates cheaper than a hand wax on that race car of yours." Timmy was really feeling it.

I was not. But I knew that if I could make it the next seven or eight miles to the safe haven that was my loft, this news would sink in and sooth my nerves about the same time the pills would. "Alright kid, I'll try to stop by."

In the minute that it took me to navigate my way up two ramps to my parking space, a calm came over me. Hadn't thought about the money from the bank the entire way. I looked to the the half zipped backpack overflowing with hundreds and the .357. It was a big haul.

After my post robbery ritual of eating pills and shower beers before counting the money I snatched back from Uncle Sam that day, I felt invincible. I'd driven like a maniac and outrun the cops, my plan was full of holes, yet I was not. The thought of stopping to see Timmy shooting scenes that night had my spirits soaring. Until I remembered a critical detail.

I left the fuckin' Mr. Cotter wig and the fuckin' Tom Selleck mustache in the fuckin' Mercedes. It was a problem. I had to call Gato.

"Yo, what up fool," he answered.

"Gato, you gotta tell your boy to forget about the car."

"What's up? He said he got up wit' you this morning, everything was cool."

"Nah man, not that. Tell him not to go back to get it."

"Yeah, right. I got you dog."

"Tell him it's a burn job and I'll square it with him later. You understand what I'm sayin', kid?"

"Yeah, yeah, I got you dog. I'll hit him up now…you straight Mick?"

There it was again, Mick. Fuckin' Gato. "Yeah kid, I'm good. Call your boy. I'll get up wit you in a minute."

One hundred fourteen thousand and eighty-nine dollars. Someone must have taken money for doughnuts and coffee from the lone bundle of one's in the safe. Had to be Phil. The coward.

Spent the rest of the afternoon and evening flipping through the local TV stations, see if there was anything on the news about my day at the office. Most led with a story of a high-speed chase on the 5. It happened between noon and one thirty. I'd made it to Commerce by one thirty. The police were in pursuit of a man who'd robbed a bank in Anaheim. I couldn't believe it. If I hadn't acted like a man on fire and kept the pedal to the metal for thirty miles I might have been involved in the chase in some way. As I watched the footage on the various newscasts I envisioned the SRT8 in the middle of a chase that ended with the typical outcome. Apprehended. The other bank robber in

Orange County that day ended up running over a spike strip near Norwalk. He was heading northwest on the 5, same as me. Destiny spoke to me in a lustful purr, 'ride this thing out, kid… you are destined for a higher purpose'.

One station had a twenty second spot about a bank in Laguna Hills, replete with a photo of the bank. But not of the perp who they described as white or Hispanic, between five foot nine and six three, between one hundred fifty and two hundred pounds. No mention of the getaway vehicle, no surveillance photo. My confidence was bolstered. Maybe I was a ghost. A six foot, two inch, two hundred twenty pound ghost. Maybe a hundred ninety now, I thought as I swallowed a fistful of Oxycontin.

Waiting for the drugs to dissolve in my stomach to numb the senses and silence the pain, I thought back to words from another time; we are creatures of habit, for better or worse, and habit is our salvation and demise all the same.

Opened the safe, took out the envelope and sat back on the sofa. I knew that it was not real, but Jackie's smell overtook my world as I unfolded the letter.

The words stayed out of focus. It was an intentional move. I folded it up and put it back in the safe, under the hefty bundles of cash from the idiotic day previous. Tears came in a blinding rush, blurring the room around me. I grabbed pen and paper.

Jackie,

I am heartbroken…haunted knowing that these days are numbered….these days are sad ones but they still hold promise and possibility. Through despair and destruction we still have free will…but simply being alive doesn't always afford us this power, kid. The future is blackened in my mind's eye as I write these words. Destruction. Looking at this word on the page I'm racked of anguish and torment…my nerves frayed. But Jackie, destruction is a precursor to creation…….I am devastated by the way I've treated you. Cynical for me to think that I've always had nothing but the best of intentions for your heart. Intentions are specters, sinister and latent lies that should not replace genuine and sincere acts of love and kindness. How the fuck did we get here? That question comes up a hundred times a day as I rush headlong toward a destination that doesn't exist. We share more than one affliction to be sure. I hope that by the time you are reading these words that your soul is addicted only to the quest for peace. Peace of mind, peace of body…….shut the door. The future never comes and the past is only real if you let it be. Only now exists. Make the most of it. Beauty is all around you Jackie, you don't even have to look for it…but if you do, you'll find it heals all….remember this. I haven't read your letter yet… don't know if I ever will. I already know your words and seeing them on the page……don't know if I can handle it…. My love for you will remain when I am long gone. For whatever it's worth……….

-Mickey

CHAPTER 26
HASIDIC HOLLYWOOD DEBUT

The day after the Chase Bank in Laguna, I bought a shoulder holster and a box of ammo from a sporting goods store in San Fernando. Spent the rest of the day driving to the furthest reaches of the Valley. I found my next bank near the Ventura Freeway, Calabasas, and the following morning I was meeting once again with Spantos. The Scarecrow.

The job in Calabasas was a revelation. No longer did I fear the police showing up on the scene while I was either still inside or on my way out. Having the pistol on me gave me another option. I stayed in the bank for longer than any of the previous times, probably a full two minutes. In that time my mind was made up to live and die by the gun. The gun that was not loaded. A strange thing occurs when a man comes to grips with his own mortality and knows that death can happen in the next minute or two. Knowing that suicide by cop would be my fate should the heat draw down on me, a massive weight was lifted.

The 'Bank Robbery in Calabasas' showed up on every newscast, complete with testimonials from customers that were inside the bank. It marked my Hollywood debut. There were photos of the armed robber dressed as a Hasidic rabbi. Didn't matter that the disguise was good, paranoia tightened its grip.

The next three weeks became a blur. Lost track of how many banks I'd hit and of how many pills I'd eaten. The gentleman bank robber working the system of bank protocol morphed into a legitimate desperado brandishing a .357. I was armed and knew the law would eventually catch up to me.

I left the loft behind, packed my car half full of clothes, grabbed the safe, and went to stay in a hotel near Malibu. It was too early in her rehab stint to have visitors, but I wanted to be near Jackie and stare out at the same horizon, smell the sea. I stayed in a different oceanside hotel every night thereafter. At night I walked the beach trying to remember back to a time of tranquility. Memories were fading fast, soon I would only think of Jackie getting better as I got worse.

Began to revel in the role of outlaw. Some days I hit two banks, different areas, driving the G-ride half the day. I was taking bigger risks, no doubt about it, but the rewards were also piling up. Was averaging fifty grand a job, but wielding the pistol meant the heists were now armed bank robbery, takeover style. Addicted to more than the drugs. I was hooked on action, strung out on easy money and the control I felt when the job was in the rearview.

I was staring down a different reality, operating without an end game on my own terms. Paranoid to spend more time than necessary in public, I searched the internet and found surveillance photos of myself on crime websites, including F.B.I. most-wanted bulletins. I was sure that my days of remaining anonymous were numbered. Sooner or later there'd be a name to go with the photos.

I met with Timmy at out of the way spots, a burger joint or a pub. I'd give him more money and he'd show me scenes on his MacBook. I had to feed him lies about why I couldn't make it to set. Run the risk of Timmy being an accomplice by association and it would all be for naught. He never pressed the issue. This kid was really doing it. He was even rewriting some of the script as he went, he was obsessed. I was proud knowing that I had a hand in something creative.

I wanted to emerge from the darkness of this hellish crime spree. But I had to keep going until I had enough dough to finish the movie and make a dash for somewhere to lay low for a while, let the dust settle. Maybe even let my body heal. I had visions of a beachside bungalow, eating healthy and sleeping the days away in the shade of massive palm trees, a good book open on my chest, maybe Steinbeck or Leonard.

Some times these visions included having Jackie by my side. We would be licking each other's wounds, spending the nights strolling in the sand, making no mention of the past or the future. We would simply be. But every time I let myself get caught up in this dream I'd become overwhelmed by the truth. My physical existence was a constant reminder of the future.

CHAPTER 27
PENNIES ON THE DOLLAR

The sunlight was coming through the tattered blinds of the latest beachside fleabag, illuminating bits and pieces of the disparate room. I shuddered. Hadn't talked to Jackie since I dropped her off in Malibu and the month I paid for was almost up. Jumped out of the bed like I was late for school and phoned Malibu. Told the director that I wanted to see Jackie. He said it wasn't a problem whatsoever. Again I thought he may have pocketed the cash and that her name did not appear in the books.

Took me two hours to drive up the coast from Seal Beach. I checked myself in the mirror a hundred times, disgusted with the shape I was in. Jackie would know. Obvious that I was strung out, I wondered if they'd even let me see her. When I arrived the director was waiting for me at the front doors. He was alone and I followed him though the palatial compound that reminded me of a place a Colombian drug lord might live. Decor was classical Mediterranean, the main corridor was spacious, it led to an open aired atrium with a miniature replica of the Fountain Trevi in Rome. Even had a million coins lining the bottom of the shallow pool. Maybe people tossed them in knowing that they'd return someday.

We came to an open terrace where there were groups of three and four seated at various tables. The sun was shining brilliant and the clouds drifted over the ocean. An ominous feeling came over me. I was high on drugs and I felt the world looking at me, picturing the antichrist. Then I saw her.

Off of the terrace in a garden area, under a gnarly oak tree on a berm, she was sitting on a bench by herself, reading a book and smoking a cigarette. The director left my side and walked away. Her face came alive when she looked up and saw me. As I got nearer she set the book down, stood, her head tilted to one side, arms hung nervously at her sides, her smile began to quiver. We hugged and eyes well up, my mouth went dry and my throat ached. Sunglasses still on, the embrace was tight but silent for what seemed like an hour.

I took a step back and gave her a once over. Her health had returned, skin was clear, her eyes vivid and brilliant. I could barely steel myself, my mind raced. We sat side by side on the bench and she was first to speak.

"I would ask how you've been Mick but I don't want to insult your intelligence," she said, her hand rubbing my thigh, her eyes searching my face.

"Don't worry for me, kid. How are you?"

"I'm well."

"What are you reading?"

"Right now? Tom Robbins. My third in three days by him. His writing reminds me of you when you're clowning around, weaving stories for my entertainment."

"Yeah," I let out a small laugh. "Like the times when we smoke the good weed and I would start the story then we'd go all night, collaborating on the plot until it would get too ridiculous to finish?"

She started in on a girlish giggle, "we'd always end it with… don't you remember?"

"Then he or she died," I said then paused. We then said in unison, "The end," and laughed for a moment.

"My mother came to visit me."

"Wow. From New York?"

"She was sad to be sure, but…not disappointed by me. I told her about you."

My heart sank. If Jackie had done that a month and a half ago I would've felt warm about the fact that she told her mother about seeing an older guy and that I was a good man. Might have done things differently. That time had passed.

"I told her that you saved my life….that I want to marry you some day."

Some day. Hearing those words from her mouth was devastating. Confessing my sins right then and there would probably be the death of her, I felt it in my bones. "You should go back and stay with her for awhile, Jackie. Get your mind right, heal, get lost in something productive or creative."

"I want to be with you, Mickey. You fixed me. Come to New York, we can get a place together, near my mother. You can write and I can nurse you back to health. We'll fuck until you're clean. Come on, Mick. A fresh start for both of us."

She had stars in her eyes. She really believed in this story. "I'll think about it, kid. Timmy started shooting the movie while I've been busy scaring up more investors. I'm sure we're gonna run over budget but we should be good," I regretted it as soon as it left my lips..

"Run over because you paid for this," she said shaking her head, staring at the sky.

More lies, "not even, don't sweat a thing, Jack. Talked my way into a huge discount with the guy that owns this place, what's his name, uh.."

"Dr. Daniels?"

"I think so. Told him about the movie, he said he's also an actor...anyways."

"You got a part in 79th Street for him?"

Relieved that Dr. Daniels wasn't female I pressed the bet, "yeah, I already started writing the character. He might even wanna throw a few bucks in the pot, get a producer's credit, back end points." She bought it and I hated myself. "Paid pennies on the dollar for a month in Malibu."

"Really? That's great news Mick. I want to go see the production when I get out of here in a few days. Can we do that?"

"I thought you were going to be with your mother?"

"She hasn't even bought the ticket for me yet, she said to let her know what day I wanted to leave."

Thought to myself for a few seconds, then said, "sure thing, baby, we can do that. I think Timmy'll be filming a couple of scenes out in the Valley around that time." That wasn't a lie, he was going to use a Taqueria in Pacoima, after-hours for three consecutive nights. He made a great deal, got the location for free as long as he'd put the owner's three sons in the scenes. They'd play the parts of gangbangers, which Timmy said they were perfect for. But it was another lie that I'd be taking Jackie to the set.

Her body language shifted, she spoke soft, "hey Mickey?"

I knew what she was going to ask before the words came out of her mouth. "What's up, kid?"

"How bad are you?"

"I'll be alright." Thinly veiled truths, swathed in disclaimers of deceit. I was toeing the line, one step closer to the lair where my mother lived.

We sat there and talked for another hour. She told me about the people she'd met and the books she'd read. I steered the conversation back to her any time she'd asked me about the goings on in my life. She'd told me what those first four or five days were like and how it was so awful that she swore to never return to that hellish place. She told me that the sun seemed to finally shine into her room by the tenth day. Listening to her talk and hearing the tone of her voice made me content, if only for the moment. Made me feel that maybe there'd be a silver lining at the end of my trip down this self-destructive path.   That maybe the purpose of my sojourn through hell was actually to do right by people that had purity and truth in their hearts.

Driving Highway One back toward the city, a plan was taking shape in my mind. I remembered a street in Pasadena that had several banks on one long city block. Probably eight or nine I was sure of. Started to make my way there and hope that the plan would unfold of it's own volition by the time I'd sighted my next job. Maybe my last one.

CHAPTER 28
CHATEAU MARMONT

By the time I'd reached Pasadena the business day had passed and the banks were closed. But my memory had served me right. Drove Lake Street two times. The area would not be ideal because of its heavy foot traffic, but the getaway route was prime. Two blocks from the 210, and it split off to the 134 just a mile west from where I would enter. The banks were not stand-alone buildings in a suburban setting or storefronts of strip malls. This would be the first time I'd hit a bank that was part of a main business thoroughfare. There was a Starbucks on the far northwest corner, I parked a hundred feet down a side street and went inside to grab a coffee. Took it to go.

Standing outside the coffee shop it came to me. I was staring at three banks, all side by side. Three nationwide chains, and each of them had branches in other locales that I'd already taken down. It would be my last job, and I'd go into all three of them, one after another. I would have to be in and out of each bank with precision and discipline. If I left the G-ride exactly where I was parked for the Starbucks I could be driving in either direction down the 210 thirty seconds after the door of the third bank closed behind me. "Fuck it," I said out loud. It got my heart racing, thinking that no matter how much the take would be, I was done. Three banks in one day, a personal best. The plan was self aggrandizing and narcissistic. Couldn't resist a grand finale.

I was an avid reader since I was four years old. My father developed an appetite for literature and self-education during his time in the hospital after Vietnam. Boxes of books and magazines filled the closets and doubled as TV stands and end tables. Many of them checked out from libraries and never returned, the only thing on my old man's rap sheet.

Fascinated with National Geographic, I was studying a picture of Maasai warriors surrounding a lion with their spears raised, and it just happened. I started reading. At least that's how the story went according to my Pops. I read *The Chronicles of Narnia* when the other kids learned ABC's. Jules Verne and Jack London before I could throw a baseball, on to Hunter S. Thompson, Vonnegut and Bukowski by the time the first hairs sprouted on my balls. I didn't understand most of the characters' drives and ethoses at the time, but the stories kept me wanting more.

By the time I'd come to Los Angeles the internet had become the lazy person's library. Holding fast to the past, I preferred books for research over punching words, even misspelled, into a search bar on a fucking laptop. That seemed too easy. But it was too delicious for a curious mind to resist.

Down a rabbit hole that began with crime in Hollywood, I came across the history of the Chateau Marmont. In no time I had painted a mental image of the place as being sort of a weigh station on the way to hell. So many legends, so many cautionary tales. It would be the perfect place to search for inspiration.

Entering the lobby my nerves calmed by the lighting and decor of the historic hotel. It felt like a place where I could disappear, at least for a night or two. It made sense to me why this had been the setting for so many stories of decadence and scandalous behavior. Nothing pretentious about the place, deep dark browns in the leather and wood, gothic mixed with classical architecture. Even an outlaw that had been all over the news lately felt anonymous. I took a suite for three nights, paid cash and checked in using my brother's driver's license as I.D.

The suite had seen better days. The furnishings were probably originals from when the Hotel was built some eighty years ago. The lighting was dim and the carpet threadbare, the room had a view of Sunset Boulevard from a small balcony. It was perfect.

The cool night smelled of distant forest fires but the sky to the south and east was clear. I could see a slice of the downtown skyline to the east and West Hollywood to the west. Smoking a cigarette, I felt like I was somebody other than myself. Made the easy decision to stay for a couple of days, enjoy this place before my curtain call in Pasadena. Maybe even plan the triple heist for the day Jackie left Malibu. It was probably best for her if I'd vanish from her life for good but I longed for her company. I tried to think of a way to salvage our love story but I couldn't see past my last job.

Put everything on the back burner, popped some pills, took a shower and thought about going downstairs, elbow up to the bar. But the thought of such a social setting felt like a dagger of betrayal after all the lies I'd fed Jackie. Opted for solitude and ordered room service.

I followed my routine of hotel living and turned on the television to scan the newscasts. I was sure there'd be nothing about me that night, but paranoia reared its insidious head. KTLA ran a one-minute piece about a rash of bank robberies in the LA area as of late. It focused on the robbers being bolder and more violent than in the past. Mid-story, a surveillance photo of me popped up, then a knock on the door. Forgot where I was for a split second, and almost made a dash for the balcony. I turned off the TV and answered the second knock on the door.

A woman wheeled the cart carrying the porterhouse and Johnnie Walker Blue. She was shapely, sexy even in her uniform that was as outdated as the furnishings. I told her to wheel it to the table. She took a quick glance at my face and smiled politely but the look in her eyes reflected what I saw in the mirror after my shower. I looked like I felt. Dracula on drugs. I tipped her three c-notes on a four hundred dollar tab. Throwing cash around helped me cope with my shame.

Tried to force down a few bites of the steak, but after a half glass of the primo scotch my liver felt like Mike Tyson had used it for a heavy bag. Alcohol no longer mixed in harmony with the pills to give me a euphoric flight through the night. Hadn't been drinking the hard stuff for a while. The last time ended with me puking and shitting blood for the next day and a half. It was all part of the sadomasochist that I'd become. Finished that bottle in the next two hours, swigs going down my throat like the flame from an acetylene torch. I blacked out some time in the night.

I came to the next evening, so sick that I spent the next few hours writhing on the bathroom floor. It was an ugly scene and I was the star. With diluted blood streaks and bile running down my bare chest, it was a horror show. When I checked into the hotel I had designs on being disciplined and meticulous in plotting this job. I was going to return to Pasadena the next day and do some more scouting, clock stoplights, make contingency plans in case the original fell apart. Staring into the mirror at a creature that used to be me, I just wanted to get it over with.

The moon became my sun. Didn't leave the hotel for the three nights I paid for. During the days the drapes were drawn, the lights remained off, the television stayed on without pause. Paranoia was suffocating me, I couldn't even call Gato to arrange a G-ride or order room service. Couldn't bear the thought of that beautiful woman wheeling the cart into the suite, trying to avoid looking at me. I had no dignity, no shame. Only forty Oxy's left. Eighty milligrams a piece.

I'd been staring at the pistol on the coffee table in the sitting area by the balcony. It had only one bullet in the revolving cylinder. Thought of throwing it over the balcony, I didn't trust the impulsive alter ego that was calling the shots these days. Instead, I stuck it in my mouth, and without hesitation I pulled the trigger.

CHAPTER 29
JUST BE COOL, KID

Jackie was supposed to leave Malibu at noon. Sent a text message the night before to the director saying I'd pick her up. I left the Chateau Marmont before sunrise and drove to my loft for the first time in almost a month. Once inside, the paranoia disappeared, replaced by the familiar feel of business-like bravado. I unpacked my clothes and returned the safe to its original spot. The sense of safety boosted my confidence and before I knew it I was dressed and driving north on the 110 to Pasadena.

Just like my first job, I'd be using the fastest getaway car yet. The SRT8. I was dressed as a Marine recruiter; canvas hi-top combat boots, fatigue pants, oversized aviator glasses, floppy hat, all camo, desert issue, except for the plain gray t-shirt that simply said USMC. I wore this outfit with guilt, felt disrespectful to buddies of mine that had served in Iraq. But it would be perfect for this job.

The Santa Ana winds had all but died out, the smell of burning forests infected the stagnant hazy air at the feet of the San Gabriel Mountains making it feel hotter than the seventy-five degrees it said on the dashboard.

It was ten thirty a.m. when I parked exactly where I'd done a few days earlier. Made a split second decision not to leave it running like usual. A headline flashed through my mind, 'BANK ROBBBER NABBED: GETAWAY CAR STOLEN WHILE INSIDE PASADENA BANK'. Took the keys with me and laughed as I exited the car, leaving the door slightly ajar. With the pistol inside the moneybag, stuffed into the side pocket of the cargo pants, I walked past the Starbucks, then hooked a left at the corner, only one person on the sidewalk for as far as I could see. He was eyeballing me as we neared one another. A hundred feet from the front door of Bank number one, I stared past him.

The young man stopped right in front of me, "hey man," he said, then raised his hand to his forehead in a military salute. "I mean, sir."

He was probably only nineteen or twenty years old. I stopped and did my best to stay in character. Hadn't the slightest clue of protocol in this situation outside of what I'd seen in movies. I saluted back.

"I just enlisted yesterday, sir," he said, standing soldier erect.

"That's great son. When do you report?"

"I'm not sure yet. My brother is First Division Infantry out at Pendleton,   sir.   Gunnery   Sergeant   Marcanio.   Dominic Marcanio."

"He's a good man, your brother," I said in a guilt stricken feign of knowledge at the mention of his brother with the same name as mine. "Well, good luck, kid."

He gave me a puzzling look. I saluted him, and he saluted back. Nodded my head and he nodded back. I continued walking and my skin boiled with uneasiness. The brief conversation just a short distance from the three banks made me nervous. The plan was to work my way back to the car, but now I wanted to put some time between the encounter with the recruit and entering the first bank. I continued past the banks, glancing into the windows. Saw a customer inside the first one and decided to circle the long city block to buy time. I got to the end of the sidewalk and turned right, crossing Lake Street. Didn't want to make another pass in front of the Starbucks, for all I knew the newly enlisted Marine had gone in for a frappuccino.

I was shaken. My thoughts raced like never before, vacillating between pulling the plug on the three banks, proceeding as planned, and sticking the .357 in my mouth, pulling the trigger until I don't find an empty chamber. Wires beyond frayed, my heartbeat seemed to drown out the sound of the world as I strode like a mad man down the idyllic residential street in Pasadena.

The final leg of the lap brought me to a tree covered side street. Approaching the sunlight at the end of the block, I could see the SRT8 just past the Starbucks. My brain was redlining and I stopped ten yards from the intersection. The thumping of my heartbeat turned into white noise when I noticed I was standing right in front of another bank. The name of it was painted on the window like it would be somewhere in small-town USA. PASADENA TRUST. The entrance was five feet in front of me and the shade from a giant oak provided natural cover from Lake Street. As if I'd forgotten about the other three banks, the brain switched to autopilot, the path of least resistance won out.

I slipped baseball gloves on, pulled the moneybag from my cargo pants, and drew the .357 as I was entering the bank. As soon as I saw the layout of the bank I knew it was a mistake. Too late. The teller, a middle-aged Hispanic man, raised his hands skyward as I approached the counter, pistol in one hand, moneybag in the other. I placed the bag on the counter and said nothing, he was already filling it with handfuls of money. Didn't need to jump the counter, it was only ten feet long, I simply walked around it. Making the turn my heart stopped and a ringing in my ears became a deafening shrill. I was staring through an entranceway to the larger room. In plain sight was an armed security guard with his back to me, standing near the front door about seventy feet away.

I had failed to notice this bank that was just across the street from the Starbucks when I cased the job.   Must have been focused on the three side-by-side smaller banks.   Fuckin drug addict dumb fuck!

I made two hurried steps and stood near the Hispanic teller, held the gun on him and said, "where's the money drawer?"

"I don't know what you're talking about sir," he said, hands shaking as he kept emptying the teller drawer, which held much more cash than a typical one.

"The fuckin' day safe, the fuckin' auxiliary drawer, where you get the money to fill this drawer.   Where…" and right then I realized where I was.   The side street entrance was for businesses and vendors and the area through the doorway was the main branch, the place where regular customers did their banking.   I snapped, snatched the moneybag from him, which was full, then he handed me a large bundle of twenties.   I bolted, stuffing the last bundle into the bag as I circled the counter like an agility drill at football practice and lowered my shoulder into the door, it flew open.   The second I crossed the threshold of the bank's door to the sidewalk I heard a pop, it sounded like a shot from a small caliber pistol.

Within seconds I was gasping for air and struggling to maintain my balance as I staggered into the intersection, making my way to the SRT8.   The .357 in my left, the moneybag was burning my right hand inside a cloud of red smoke.   I could barely see, my eyes were spewing tears, nose a geyser of snot, and I was using my hands to keep me from falling to the pavement.

I collapsed in front of the Starbucks, a hundred feet from the SRT, dropped the gun and fumbled the bag trying to pull the dye pack out which by now had expended its contents.   The world went into slow motion, silent as I began to crawl, pistol and scalding moneybag in tow.   I wiped the bodily fluids from my face with my pistol hand, and in one glimpse of clear vision, saw a man slowly backpedaling, filming me with his phone.   I pointed the gun at him as I made it to my feet.   He leapt to his right as a car slammed on its brakes, stopping just short of running him over.

Somehow I made it into my car and got it started. I could barely see or breathe, the military grade tear gas from the dye-pack did a real job on me. Tossed the red, crumpled bag of money into the back seat as I took off, sideswiping two cars headed in the opposite direction. The smell in the car was suffocating, rolled down all four windows.

The gas pedal made the SRT8 roar, but my vision was blurred so bad I was slamming the brakes every few seconds. In the silent mayhem I had no wits about me. At the end of the street I made a right. Clipping mirrors from parked cars for two blocks, I realized that the expressway was the other direction. I hooked a right, then another and was back on Lake headed toward the 210. My eyes were still on fire but I could see a little better. I was tearing my disguise off, first the hat, then the shirt, which was tie-dyed red, and finally the gloves. The aviators had fallen off during the dye pack dash and I didn't have a clue where they fell. Didn't care as I neared the intersection that I staggered across amidst a red cloud two minutes earlier. The cars in front of me were swerving to the left, being slowly waved past a police car that was diagonally parked at the crux of the streets. I had no choice. Couldn't turn around. Couldn't park. I rolled up the tinted windows, placed the pistol near my crotch and followed the car in front of me closely at less than five miles an hour through the intersection. The cop didn't look at me but I got a good look at his face in profile. It was my brother Dominic. Everything appeared to be happening in a dream as he waved to an officer getting out of a squad in front of the Starbucks. I rolled right past but almost stopped. A hundred yards past the intersection an unmarked cruiser was flying toward me, interior flashers ablaze, siren sounding from somewhere under the hood deafening my ears, our cars passed like ships in the night. I snapped out of it and floored the gas pedal.

Hit the entrance ramp for the 210 heading east, my mind

struggling to think of what to do next, I could only think to go as fast and as far as I could. I merged into traffic, rolled the windows back down to let the rush of air soothe the burn on my eyeballs and face, then heard the unmistakable sound of helicopter blades. I pushed the SRT8 to its limit, hitting a hundred and sixty by the time I made an exit ramp a quarter mile from where I'd entered. Flew down the ramp, braking hard and downshifting near the bottom, and cut the wheel sharply to do a 180 under the overpass, out of sight from the chopper. I nearly rolled the car but somehow made it to the other side, straightened the beast out on the westbound ramp, and merged into traffic at over a hundred. I cut across five lanes to the far left, then weaved in and out like a video game. Reckless fashion just like everything in my life.

"Timmy, where are you at?" I barked into the phone.

"I'm by the pool, where the fuck you at..."

"Stay there, kid, I'll be there in a while."

"Cool, grab a few…"

I dropped the phone as I swerved at the last second to hit the 134. It wouldn't be the shortest route to Downtown, but It would be the quickest at the rate I was driving. The morning's drugs seemed to have been nullified by the horror show I'd just been a part of. Sweating, my skin was still burning from the gas, the ringing in my ears was drowning out all sound, and the only thing I could visualize at the moment was Jackie sitting on that bench in Malibu, waiting for me.

Heading down the Glendale Freeway, traffic was still light. I searched for the phone underneath the seat and found it after I'd almost hit the guardrail. I called Malibu.

"Salvation," said the voice on the other end.

"Yeah, let me talk to…."

"Is this Mr. Fortunato?"

My temples began to pound at hearing my name, "it is. Is this…" I cut myself off. It was him, the director, and I could never remember his name because it was something generic

American like Michael Smith or Matt Jones. It was nondescript, which wasn't always a bad thing.

"This is Craig Gore, at Redemptive Measures. Jackie is talking to her counselor right now. She will be finished in about fifteen or twenty minutes. Will you be arriving early?"

He seemed like a nice enough guy. Wanted to tell him to cut the shit though and that I knew he pocketed the cash. Instead I was the outlaw version of passive aggressive. "Put her on the phone, Craig."

"She'll be finished..."

"Listen here dude, if Jackie isn't speaking to me on this line in the next ten seconds I'm gonna come to that fuckin' fraud in Malibu, wipe the fuckin' self serving grin off of your fuckin' face and make sure you choke to death on your teeth."

"Mickey?" Jackie said in a quizzical tone.

Tears cascaded down my cheeks in that instant. I was not sobbing. Body didn't quake, nose didn't run, lips. steady. "Hey kid, how you feel?"

"Hey..." her voice fell off at that.

"Listen. I want you to know something," I said as I searched for the words.

"What's up Mick?"

"I'm not gonna make it today"

"Ok."

We listened to each other breath for ten seconds, "go home, kid." Impulse told me to throw the phone out the window and leave it at that. But my shaking hand held it to my ear for another few seconds.

"Wait. No..."

CHAPTER 30
TAKE THIS, KID

M y body was numb by the time I took the left from Seventh Street onto Main. Expected to see cruisers parked in front of my building but there were none. I hit the overhead button and the garage door opened from a half block down. As always, felt that comforting blanket wrapping itself over my shoulders as I approached my parking space. Knew it was an apparition now, but I was grasping for strings.

Entered my loft but didn't close the door behind me, emptied the money from the safe into my backpack, tucked the letters into my cargo pocket and rushed to the rooftop.

Timmy was alone on the pool deck. He had his phone to his ear and a bottle of Corona in the other when he saw me. He continued talking as I approached. "Hey Frank, I gotta go, the head of the studio just walked in, I'll call you back on that permit in five minutes," he was saying, eyes hidden behind Blues Brothers shades as he spread his arms as if to say, 'My guy!'

"Take this, kid," I said holding the backpack five inches from his chest.

He set his beer down on a small table next to his chair and let his arms come close to grasping the backpack, but stopped and said, "what the fuck is this? Don't tell me this is the still beating heart of that scumbag mother of yours." The sarcasm was spot on for the moment. I wanted to snatch him out of the lounger and give him a kiss. Timmy understood me even if he didn't yet.

"Take this and do something great. I'm gonna bounce." We were locked in a stare of a thousand miles. It was understood. I turned to leave but stopped, "Call Jackie from time to time for me, would ya?"

"Mick,"

"Yeah, guy," I said over my shoulder.

"Call me when you get to wherever you're goin'."

I paused for a second, wanted to tell him everything, but I couldn't look back. He would know the story before too long.

———

Entered my loft, walked to the center of the floor, stopped, felt the heavy piece of steel in the pocket rubbing against my knee, looked around, then left.

I should have locked the door behind me and had a beer or ten.

When the elevator doors opened at the second floor of the parking garage, I stepped out only to see five men, plain-clothes cops to be sure. I approached. They froze.

"Officers."

———

Some time during the next night I was brought to a hospital by a couple of Los Angeles County Deputies. I was hunched over, the cuffs dug into my wrists. Pains shot through my ribcage, and the warm sensation of liquid shit spread throughout the pants of my county issued blues against the cold plastic seat of the squad car. I recognized the song Deputies were listening to, the drums and guitar spoke to me. Even as I was trying to keep the rest of my bodily fluids at bay, the Red Hot Chili Peppers soothed my soul as my body convulsed, its response to not receiving its regimen of medication. I thought I was going to die.

I contorted and pleaded on the gurney. A nurse took initiative and displayed open animosity as she took control of the rolling bed, escorting me down the hallway. Feeling the cuffs on either side but not a struggle in my being, we locked eyes for a moment. Was it empathy? Was I delusional? Or hallucinating. I didn't see it coming, she stuck a needle in me and the pain was gone. My skin dried in a couple of minutes and my body relaxed. The immediate comfort I felt led me into a dreamscape. That nurse would reappear in dreams for the rest of my life.

When I finally came to, the left side of my face was in a puddle of drool, resting on a concrete bench in a holding tank of the Pasadena courthouse. I heard "Fortunato" and like a bad dream I rose to a reality that would soon become my world. "Fortunato," a stern female voice said again as my vision came into focus on the heavyset deputy at the bars. I walked toward her with as much vigor as I could summon. A buzzing noise, then a mechanical sound of the lock disengaging. The door opened.

I walked into the courtroom handcuffed and shackled. Jackie was sitting in the cheap seats, the benches at the back of the courtroom. She watched the deputy help me into the seats of the empty jury box. I'd soon come to find out this was standard for criminals like me, a county inmate with a federal hold on him. Continuances for years.

I looked like a menace to society in my ill-fitting county blues, wrapped in chains. Seated next to Jackie on that bench was a future I'd never see. There was no mistake that the woman beside her was her mother. Jackie in twenty-five years. A youthful face, void of the signs of a life of chaos and despair. Wild and bright eyes framed by the same mane of golden hair.

As the bailiff began the proceedings and the judge sat, an

eerie calm came over me. The words from the judge faded to white noise as I looked at Jackie. Her face was swollen, her eyes weary and watery. Our eyes met and she smiled, but I didn't gesture.

I was still in L.A. County Jail a year later and the deal to bound me over to federal custody was made. Was housed in Twin Towers for a month waiting for the transfer and hadn't received a letter from Jackie in nine months so when 'Fortunato' rang out at mail call, my heart jumped. The sender: Cassavetes, 610 S. Main St., L.A.

Yo Mick,

How the fuck you holding up in there, 'kid'? I know I don't have to say it but, I miss you man. You're a crazy mother-fucker...Fuck...Man, I guess I'm searching for the words. Anyways, after you handed me that backpack I felt like I was tossed out into the universe without a compass or a calling card. Lost without my brother. After a cool minute the dust settled and nobody "official" came a knockin......your words came to me like voices in my head and I knew what I had to do. I finished what we started.........79th Street is goin' to Sundance!!! I know you got some time in front of you but when you do get around to seeing it you're gonna be fuckin proud, my guy. It turned out just like you envisioned it. Raw and dark, but funny and beautiful.

Listen, I'm following your case the best I can. I'll put money on your books for canteen until those doors swing open and we can grab a case of Miller Lites and see where the road takes us. Til then...

Just be cool kid,

Timmy

ABOUT THE AUTHOR

The son of a long distance drifter, Josh has been on the run since 1975. From Cody, Wyoming to Los Angeles to Amalfi by way of Chicago, he's always fought out of the dark corner. After twenty years of blood, sweat and adrenaline as a union ironworker in the Windy City, he wrote a letter to a lady he met on his latest sojourn. He wrote this novel on a rooftop in Conca Dei Marini. Josh and Andreina have three cats…yeah…he married the girl, and she's followed the nomad around the world ever since.

CPSIA information can be obtained
at www.ICGtesting.com
Printed in the USA
LVHW051235300623
751146LV00005B/470